Mrs Sanders
161 Cromwell Road
Ware
HERTFORDSHIRE
SG12 7LH

This book — the first of a two-part volume about the St. Ives Mining District is a tribute to the painstaking researches of the author. At a time when more and more of the industrial history of St. Ives and district falls prey to the relentless onslaught of touristic and housing speculative development it has become imperative that a full mining survey should be published. Here, in the old parishes of St. Ives, Lelant, Towednack, Zennor and Morvah, amidst some of the most beautiful and varied scenery in Cornwall, are the remains of an industry that dated back to Bronze Age times and extended to recent days of deep mining. The winning of tin left behind a proliferation of remains which are being increasingly obliterated.

THE ST. IVES MINING DISTRICT

By

CYRIL NOALL

VOLUME ONE

Children and Bal Maidens working at St. Ives Consols Mine c. 1870. (R.I.C.)

THE ST. IVES MINING DISTRICT

By
Cyril Noall

VOLUME ONE

DYLLANSOW TRURAN, TRURAN PUBLICATIONS
Trewolsta, Trewirgie, Redruth, Kernow

ISBN 0 907566 32 4 Hardback
0 907566 33 2 Paperback

First published 1982 by Dyllansow Truran, Redruth, Cornwall
Printed by St. George Printing Works Ltd., 1-3-5 Wesley Street, Camborne, Cornwall.
Telephone: (0209) 712354

SECTION ONE

LELANT DISTRICT

PHOTOGRAPHS

Ruins of Carn Galver Mine. (W.T.)
Repairing a damaged engine house at Wheal Sisters after it had been struck by lightning in April 1886. (R.I.C.)
Wheal Sisters. The engine house on the right is the same as that shown in the previous picture. It appears to have been taken soon after the repairs were completed, the whitish patches on the roofs corresponding to the damaged areas in No. 21.
Worvas Downs, 1904. (E.M.)
Worvas Downs. (H.C.C.) (L.E.C.)
Wheal Merth, near Trencrom. (G.) (M.)
Bowl Rock Stamps, Lelant, in the 1920's. (D.N.)
Providence Mines soon after closure, *c.* 1880. (M.) (E.A.)
Carn Galver Mine, 1885. (J.H.T.)
Trencrom Mine, *c.* 1870. (H.)
Wheal Lucy, Phillack. (C.C.L.)

PHOTO CREDITS

C.C.L. Cornwall County Library
E.M. Eddie Murt
G. Capt. Gerry
H. Messrs. N. Holman & Sons, Ltd.
J.B. Justin Brooke
J.H.T. J.H. Trounson
K.L. Kent Leddra
M. St. Ives Museum
R.I.C. Royal Institution of Cornwall
D.N. Dicon Nance

PHOTOGRAPHERS

H.S.M. Herbert S. Morris
L.E.C. L.E. Comley
S.J.G. S.J. Govier
W.T. William Thomas
H.J.H. H.J. Healey

PHOTOCOPIES

ADVERTISEMENTS

Carn Galver, 1869
Golden Bank and Wheal Chance United Tin Mining Company, 1839
East Margaret, 1865
Trencrom Mine, 1867

MISCELLANEOUS

Wheal Sisters Prospectus, 1890

ACKNOWLEDGEMENTS

I wish to express grateful thanks to all those kind friends who willingly assisted during the compilation of this book. The excellent plans and sections were drawn by Charles Smith, of Carbis Bay, and Alan Reynolds of St. Just. Charles Smith also provided some notes on the geology of the district and was actively associated with the project in various other ways. Many of the photos were made available by John H. Trounson, of Redruth, from his unique collection of Cornish mining views. The task of copying these, and other photographs, was most capably undertaken by William Thomas, of Carbis Bay. To Justin Brooke, of Marazion, I am indebted for many kindnesses; he readily consented to read the manuscript, making several suggestions for its improvement; he also supplied information from his own extensive files on some of the more elusive local mines, and compiled the valuable list of mines aranged in order of parishes.

Information and help were also given by the following: G.C. Penaluna, Scorrier; Paul Stephens, Devoran; Alan Pearson, Redruth; H.L. Douch (Curator) and Roger Penhallurick, County Museum, Truro; P.L. Hull (Archivist) and J.C. Edwards, County Record Office, Truro; Mrs. S. Balson, Librarian, Penzance (Morrab Gardens) Library; staff of St. Ives Branch, Cornwall County Library; Terry Knight, Local Studies Dept., Redruth Library; the late W.T. Harry, Penzance; E.T. Berryman, Beagletodn, Towednack; St. Ives Museum Management Committee (for use of photos and other material); Jim Hodge, St. Ives; Dicon Nance, Carbis Bay; Arthur Dale, Lelant Downs; E.W.A. Edmonds, Perranwell.

ALPHABETICAL LIST OF MINES, ARRANGED IN ORDER OF PARISHES (USING MID-19th CENTURY PARISH BOUNDARIES)

LELANT

Wheal Adelaide 1905
Wheal Alice 1873-77
Balnoon before 1758
Balnoon (1827) - 1839
Balnoon Consols Mine (1845) - 1850
Balnoon Consols Mining Company 1852-58
Bennyon 1584
Boldstamps — before 1870
Wheal Fanny Adela (1868) — (1871)
Wheal Gilbert Consols 1875-76
Wheal Grace 1756-58
Hallywoone 1584
Hawke's Point 1849-54
Wheal Hope 1844-45
South Wheal Kitty 1860-74
Wheal Kitty 1852-76
Wheal Kitty and Mary United 1858-61
Lelant Consolidated Mines (1829) - 1840
Lelant Consols 1852-67
Lelant Consols Mining Company 1844-52
Lelant Mining Company, Limited 1905-09
Lelant Syndicate, Limited 1911
Lelant Towant (1710)
Lelant Towans (1820)
Wheal Locke 1892-94
West Wheal Lucy Tin and Copper Mine 1871-76
East Wheal Margaret 1902-03
South Margaret 1872-82 and Ludgvan
South Wheal Margaret 1854-57 and Ludgvan
West Margaret 1869-71
West Wheal Margaret 1857-62
Wheal Margaret 1790
Wheal Margaret Mining Company 1840-75 and Towednack
Wheal Margery 1853-69
East Wheal Mary 1871-73
Wheal Mary (1838) - 1875
Mount Tiack Tin and Copper Mining Company 1852-56
Nance Valley Lead and Copper Mine 1860-62 (location doubtful)
Wheal Nantz 1849
Wheal North 1904
Wheal Pencrom (1869) - 1870
Polpeor Mine 1873-75
East Providence 1872
East Providence Mine 1852 — before 1857
East Providence Mining Company 1857-77
Providence Mines 1832-78 and St. Ives
South Providence (1870) - 1889
South Providence Mine (1855) - 1857
Providence United Mining Company 1882-89
Wheal Providence Copper Mine (1821)
East Wheal Reeth 1868-71
East Wheal Reeth 1857-60
East Wheal Reeth Mining Company 1850-55
Wheal Reeth 1757
Wheal Reeth (1785) — before 1812
Wheal Reeth 1812-42
Wheal Reeth 1844-67
South Wheal Speed 1850-55
Old Tincroft Mine 1855-59
Towan Mine 1855
Trelyon Bounds 1836-58
Trembethow (1825)
Trencrob-ben (or Trencrom) Tin and Copper Mine 1871 - (1875)
Trencrom Mine 1857-66
Trevarrack 1911
Trevarrack Mining Company 1869-73
Trevarrack Mining Company, Limited 1873-76
Trewartha Tin and Copper Mine 1845-52

MORVAH

Carn Galver Mine 1851-59 and Zennor
Carn Galver Mine 1874 - (1882) and Zennor
Garden Mine 1860 — before 1873
Garden Tin Mine 1853
Morvah and Zennor United Mines 1836-41 and Zennor
Morvah Consols 1851-54
Morvah Consols Tin Mining Company, Limited 1871-90
Rosemergy and Morvah Syndicate, Limited 1908-15 and Zennor
Rosemergy Cliff about 1758
Wheal Widden 1849

ST. IVES

Wheal Ayr Mine 1847-50
North Battery Tin Mine 1821
British Radium Corporation, Limited 1908-21

Carbisse 1584
Carrack Dews (1810-1838)
Carrack Dews Mine 1861-62
Carrack Dews United Mines 1853-60
Wheal Crack — before 1832
Wheal George 1832-39
Wheal Gift (1860)
Goole Pellas Mine 1876-81
Island Consols 1853
Ludgvan Lease Tin Mine Company 1853-57
Wheal Margery (1760)
Penolva Mine (1822)
Providence Mines 1907
North Wheal Providence Mining Company 1859-73
North Wheal Providence Tin and Copper Mining Company, Limited 1862-82
Providence Tin Mines, Limited 1907-15
West Providence Mine 1881-91
Wheal Racer, Limited 1907-09 and Towednack
Wheal St. Aubyn and Tregenna Mine 1847
St. Ives Consolidated Mines, Limited, 1908-25
St. Ives Consols 1818-82
St. Ives Consols (1875) - 1890
(St. Ives Copper Mines) 1687
St. Ives Mines, Limited 1917-22 and Towednack
South Saint Ives Tin and Copper Mining Company, (Limited) 1864-65
West St. Ives Mines 1866-72
St. Ives Wheal Allen 1860-68
Wheal Sarah 1838 St. Ives district; may be Gulval
Stennack Stamps — before 1876
Tasmanian Exploration Company, Limited 1904-12 and Tasmania
Thermo-Electric, Limited 1912-32
Trelyon Consolidated Mines 1849
Trenwith Mine 1905-08
Trenwith Mine 1917-20
Trenwith Stamps (1792)
Wheal Trenwith 1825-49
Wheal Trenwith 1853-57
Wheal Union 1836 and Towednack
Velenoweth Mine — before 1849 St. Ives district; may be Ludgvan
Wheal Venture 1836-39
Wheal Wellesley 1836
Western Worke 1585
Worvas Downs (1810) - (1817)
Worvas Downs 1905-09
Worvas Downs Mine 1860-72

TOWEDNACK

Billia Consols 1864-70
Bray Tin and Copper Mine (1838) - (1848)
Bray Tin Mine — 1822
Brea Consolidated Tin and Copper Mining Company, Limited 1858-1901
Wheal Bussow 1852
Wheal Buzza (1880)
Wheal Conquer 1859-61
Wheal Conquer Consols 1857
Durlo Mine 1859-64
Georgia Consols 1847-48
Georgia Consols 1850-54
Georgia Consols 1871-73
Giew, opened after 1871, closed by 1909 and Lelant
Giew 1917-22
Giew Consolidated Mines 1869 - (1871)
Wheal Lady Down and Conquer 1836
West Wheal Margaret Mining Company, Limited 1871-72
Wheal Margaret 1798
Wheal Montague Tin Mine 1851-56
Wheal Music 1844 (location unconfirmed)
Wheal Music Mine 1839
Praed Consols 1850-54
Praed Consols 1860-62
South Providence 1869-72 and Lelant
South Providence 1873-89 and Lelant
Reeth Consolidated Mining Company 1836-52
Reeth Consols 1852-59
Wheal Rose 1854-55
Rosewall Hill and Ransom United Mines 1857-80
Rosewall Hill Mine (1808) - (1815)
Rosewall Hill Mine 1838-42
Rosewall Hill Mine 1876
Rosewall Hill Mining Company 1845-50
Rosewall Stamps 1680
Roswall 1584
West St. Ives Consolidated Tin Mining Company, Limited 1868-83
Tincroft Consols 1836-41 and Ludgvan
New Tincroft United Mining Company, Limited 1876-86 and Ludgvan
Old Tincroft Consols Mining Company, Limited 1874-84
Trevega Mine 1909-15 and Zennor
Trevega Mine, Limited 1907-11 and Zennor
Trevesa and Brea Tin and Copper Mining Company, Limited 1864-73
Trevidgia Mine 1841-42
Trewey Consolidated, Limited, 1907-10 and Zennor
Trowan Consols Mine 1846-54
Tyringham Consols Mining Company 1860-64 and St. Ives

ZENNOR

Carn Galver Tin Mining Company, Limited 1871-74 and Morvah
Carnelloe 1862-66
Carnelloe Consols 1853 - (1856)
Carnelloe Mine 1871-74
Wheal Chance and Good Fortune 1844
Wheal Chance Tin Mine 1809
Cleveland Mining Company 1845-58

Wheal Dollar Mine 1823-25
Wheal Dollar Mine 1834-41

West Wheal Fanny Tin Mining Company 1852-53

North Grylls Tin Mining Company, Limited 1864
Wheal Grylls 1860-64
Gurnett's Head Mine 1843-44

Wheal Hope Mining Company 1845-48

Wheal Rose 1893
Rosevale Mine (1910) - 1912
Rosevale (Zennor) Tin Mine, Limited 1912-18

Wheal Sandwich 1836
Great Sperries Consols 1862 and Towednack
Wheal Sperries 1836 and Towednack
Great Sperries Consols Tin Mining Company 1853 and Towednack

Treen Copper mine — before 1821
Tregerthen Mine 1872
Treveal Tin and Copper Mine 1836 and Towednack
Trewey Downs Mining Company, Limited 1906-07

North United Mining Company 1843-48

Zennor Consols Tin Mine 1873-75

INTRODUCTION

The area covered by this survey embraces the old undivided parishes of St. Ives, Lelant, Towednack, Zennor and Morvah, bordering the north-western shore of the Penwith peninsula. Some of the most varied and beautiful scenery in Cornwall is to be found here, making it today a tourist's paradise, but in the past it was chiefly noted for its connection with the industries of fishing and mining. The district is bounded on the east by that part of St. Ives Bay extending from the ancient fishing port of St. Ives along an indented shore of dark headlands and contrasting golden beaches towards Lelant Towans and the western side of Hayle Estuary. The pleasant woodlands at Lelant, rising above the river, flourish in the shelter of Trencrom Hill, whilst in similar fashion Carbis Bay and St. Ives nestle below the heights of Worvas, Penbeagle and Rosewall. Beyond, the bleak moors and "high countries" of the western parishes sweep away under a wide sky towards the limits of Bolerium. To the north and west these moors command magnificent views of the Atlantic Ocean; but between them and the rugged shore lies a narrow fertile plain patterned with the complicated tracery of an ancient Celtic field system.

The area is rich in prehistoric remains, including hut circles, cromlechs and barrows. It is certain that from Bronze Age times onwards the inhabitants of West Penwith were engaged in the winning of tin, for which the district was very favourably endowed by Nature. Nearly the whole of the peninsula consists of granite; but along its shore runs a narrow band of metamorphosed killas[1] and greenstone, which attains its greatest width at Lelant, being there up to a mile and a half across, but at Rosemergy disappears altogether, the cliffs there being of granite. Around St. Ives, as at St. Just, heavily mineralised lodes traverse the killas and granite around their contact, material from which, eroded by swift-flowing streams, provided the earliest tinners with the alluvial or "stream" tin which they dug from shallow workings. In much later times deep mines were developed on these lodes, usually at or near the granite-killas junction.

In the immediate vicinity of St. Ives this contact zone occurs along an inclined plane sloping very irregularly to the E. and N.E., with an average strike of E. 20 deg. S. The killas overlies the granite, so that mines sunk at surface in the first rock often enter the second in depth. At Wheal Trenwith, for example, the contact is seen in Victory shaft 285′ below sea level; whilst at Cornish shaft and Sump shaft of St. Ives Consols, lying further to the west, it appears at 160′ and 280′ above sea level respectively. It has been calculated that the approximate dip of the granite is 15 deg. N.E. between the surface junction and Cornish shaft, and 33 deg. N.E. between Cornish shaft and Victory shaft; while below the 60 fm. level around Victory shaft the dip becomes much steeper and its strike more easterly. On one side of the contact are seen altered slates and greenstone and on the other quartz-tourmaline and greisen of various types graduating into moderately fine-grained granite. Further west, the granite becomes more coarsely crystalline with large crystals of pale pink and white felspar.

The lodes generally trend E.N.E., the cross-courses, locally termed "trawns," trending nearly N.—S. around St. Ives and a few degrees W. of N. elsewhere. Generally speaking, the lodes, when in granite, produced tin, and copper when in the overlying rocks; but there were some notable exceptions to this rule, as at Wheal Providence and Wheal Sisters, where large amounts of copper were produced from granite country. In addition to these metals, small quantities of uranium were found at Trenwith and South Providence, as well as nickel and cobalt, but except for uranium (for its associated radium) none of these was mined on a commercial scale.

The lodes in the western part of the district were relatively unimportant, and Morvah and Zennor consequently failed to develop any large mines. The principal lode systems were those which gave rise to the mines in the immediate vicinity of the town of St. Ives (Rosewall Hill, St. Ives Consols and Trenwith); south of St. Ives (Tyringham, Trelyon and Margery); Carbis Bay (Balnoon, Worvas and Providence); and the Billia-Giew-Reeth, Sisters and Merth series. In the northern part of the district the lodes cut the granite-killas junction nearly at right-angles, but in the south run sometimes nearly parallel with it. Certain of the coastal mines — notably Margery and Providence — had workings which extended beneath the sea, but were never prosecuted to any great degree there, owing, so it is said, to percolation of salt water through the sea bed, this being in marked contrast to the St. Just submarine mines, which were extremely dry. So far as these explorations went, however, they showed that the ore-shoots pitched eastwards, or away from the killas-granite contact.

An unusual feature of the district was the occurrence of large deposits of ore, quite different in character from the conventional lodes, known as "carbonas." They were found principally in Rosewall Hill, St. Ives Consols and Providence, and always in granite. The carbonas seemed to have but a tenuous relationship to the lode systems in those mines. At St. Ives Consols, for example, the carbonas were found between the Standard lode and the Bahavella lode running parallel to it on the south. These carbonas were extremely rich and their material largely decomposed, enabling it to be easily removed.

Some authorities likened these carbonas to the irregular ore-bodies in the limestone country of the lead-mining districts; but Cann[2] insisted they were nothing more than a special type of peculiar form of ordinary lodes. In St. Ives Consols they were invariably connected with the Standard lode by a vein, although this vein was very small at the point of junction, sometimes no more than two or three inches wide. The irregularly-shaped portions of the carbonas were apparently formed by the contact of a series of branch veins and the intersection of approximately E. and W. running cross-lodes, with converging cross-courses. It is not clear whether these cross-lodes belong to a later period, as the junctions show only a jumbled mass of ore, from 50 to 70 ft. wide, shading off into the country rock without any distinct boundaries. Much of this material was formed as a replacement of the enclosing rock. The cross-courses were of a subsequent period, as they fault the carbonas, parallel lodes and cross-lodes. Near the cross-courses numerous veinlets rich in cassiterite branch off from the hanging and footwall sides of the carbonas at their junction.

It therefore seems that carbonas developed at points where several lodes intersected and where the nature of the resulting fracture zone allowed the ascending tin and copper-bearing fluids to replace the severely fractured granite. Thus carbonas possess the replacement features of "pipes and flats" in that extensive replacement of country rock which did occur, but in their overall attitudes they reflected that of the adjacent lodes. It is also relevant that carbonas tend to have developed close beneath the killas-granite contact, which suggests that the resistant nature of the overlying killas tended to "bottle-up" or impound the rising mineral-bearing fluids and force them to react and replace the fractured granite.

The most spectacular of these massive ore bodies was the "Great Carbona"of St. Ives Consols, which branched off from the Standard lode at the 77 fm. level, approximately 460 ft. below the surface. Cann's description of it is worth quoting: "From the point of junction it has been worked about 900 ft. in a direction S. 40 deg. E. and has been followed downward on an incline from the horizontal of 75 deg. W. to a depth of about 600 ft. below the 57 fm. level. The character of the ore varies a good deal with depth. In the upper portion it consists of very hard and compact quartz-schorl rock with cassiterite disseminated in very minute particles. Below, it is composed of quartz and chlorite with a considerable amount of tourmaline. The cassiterite is fairly coarse and associated with a little copper pyrites and mispickel. There also occur, in the lower portions, alternate bands of fluorspar on the footwall side, highly impregnated with fairly large crystals of cassiterite."[2]

In *British Mining* (1884) Dr. Robert Hunt went very thoroughly into the meaning and origin of this curious word "carbona." Dismissing theories that it may have been derived from a Cornish (Celtic) source, he quoted the following passage from the New Testament published at the English College in Rheims, A.D. 1582, where St. Matthew, c. 27, v. 6, is rendered: "Principes, autem sacerdotum, acceptis argenteis dixerunt: Non licet eos mittere in carbonam" (But the chief priest having taken the pieces of silver, said, It is not lawful to put them into the carbona, because it is the price of blood.) The carbona was, in fact, the Treasury of the Temple where the people put in their gifts or offerings, and was thus a very appropriate term to apply to unusually large and rich bunches of ore.

The history of the development of mining at St. Ives followed much the same pattern as in other mineralised areas of Cornwall, beginning with streaming for alluvial tin deposits in the valleys and moors. Probably the best known of the ancient stream works from which the local mining industry evolved lay along the valley which runs into the town of St. Ives from the western hills. Its very name, Stennack, means tin bearing ground, the earliest form of which, spelled *Steynek*, dates from as early as 1334.[3] This stream work extended southwards from Hellesveor Moors to Balnoon, taking in the lower part of the present village of Halsetown. Another followed the course of the little rivulet which runs from the higher part of the Belyars near Carnstabba Farm, through Tregenna estate and the steep, narrow Primrose Valley to Porthminster beach. The bottoms between Providence and South Providence, at Carbis Bay, and the Nancledra, Trink and Trencrom valleys were also turned over and over again by the "old men" with their primitive tools in search of the precious black stones. Further west, there were very ancient stream works at Trewey, in Zennor, and in some of the valleys running from the western moors to the sea. Nearly all traces of these workings have disappeared, and no description exists of them; but Henwood has left an account of one very late example which was being prosecuted in the lower part of Coldharbour Moor, Towednack, around 1872. Beneath a 2½′ layer of peat appeared 3′ of granitic gravel unequally mixed with blue clay to different depths. Under this lay another strata of gravel 6½′ deep, brownish buff above and reddish brown below. The first contained small amounts of detrital cassiterite, and the second angular and fairly rounded masses of tin-bearing veinstone. The underlying bedrock was undulating and of varied hardness, moderate amounts of detrital ore being found in the depressions.[4]

The exploitation of these deposits eventually led to the discovery of the lodes from which their material had been derived, and so enabled true mining to begin. In the early years of underground mining the primitive workings were drained by adits driven from nearby valleys. As the levels began to go below adit buckets and rag-and-chain pumps were progressively used, but with continually increasing depth and extent of the workings the volume of water proved too much for such elementary forms of drainage, so water wheels were used to motivate the pumps, "flat rods" often being used to transmit their power over considerable distances.

Around the coast, lodes were readily discovered by their outcrops in the cliffs, on which adits were then driven. One of the earliest and most interesting of these was the "Western Worke," a St. Ives copper mine dating from the year 1585. The famous "Mines Royal" had a considerable interest in Cornish copper mining at this time; and ore both from St. Ives and St. Just was shipped off to Neath for smelting from St. Ives. Norden mentions "Carbisse," a mine at St. Ives in 1584; this was presumably located in the vicinity of Carbis Water, being a primitive working on the site of the later Providence Mines. Also working at that time were Bennyon and Hallywoone, in Lelant, and Roswall, in Towednack. Coffen (open cast) mining was extensively practised at this early period on Rosewall Hill, its summit being scored by deep trenches on the backs of the lodes, revealing very plainly the direction of their strike.

Around 1687 Sir Thomas Clarke and others worked copper mines in the St. Ives area. The technique of blasting was introduced into West Cornwall by a German expert about the year 1700 at Trevega Bal; whilst smelting was carried on at St. Ives in 1712 by Eswyn, and by Fayrehoven and Co. in 1714; also by Thomas Morgan. Hicks (the first St. Ives historian) writing in 1722 further mentions a copper house started by one Pollard. In those times, St. Ives was connected with St. Just by a packhorse trackway which ran more or less in a straight line over the moors and hills between; and it seems probable that these smelting works received ore from the far west as well as from the local mines.

As the mines grew deeper new techniques were developed to counter the increasing hardness of the rocks. Improved iron drills with finely tempered cutting edges were made to bore holes in the granite and overlying killas. Due to increasing hardness below the zone of weathering, shafts were sunk along the dip of the lode or its "underlie"; thus until recent times shafts were narrow and crooked depending upon the varying attitude of the lode being followed. Lodes and cross-cuts were driven by hand drilling using a "drag round" pattern of holes and black powder. With the advent of machine drilling (the widow maker) and more powerful explosives, this drag round gave way to the "pyramid cut." Stoping of the lode was either "overhand" (with the lode in the roof or back) or "underhand" (with the lode in the floor), with or without stulls. Pillars of ground were left only when the lode was uneconomic; often the roof and floor of a drive would be removed and the track supported on wooden stulls. This timber has now long rotted away and the dangers of entering these old workings is now very great and should on no account be attempted.

Steam power for pumping was introduced into one or two mines in the mid 18th century, notably at Wheal Margaret and Wheal Reeth. It is interesting to note that the original name of the Engine Inn, at Cripple's Ease, near those mines, was the Fire Engine, showing what a great impression the Newcomen machine must have made in that neighbourhood. But steam did not really come into its own until about the 1820's, from which time the mines increased rapidly in depth and output. The middle years of the 19th century saw the industry at its zenith, several thousand persons being employed both above and below ground. Then it was that the lords, like the Praeds of Trevetho, and the adventurers, like James Halse (after whom the mining village of Halsetown took its name) practised the art of transmuting base tin and copper into pure gold, while the miners grubbed for a bare pittance in the bowels of the earth and thought themselves lucky to get an occasional "sturt."

Those were busy, bustling, hard-working times, such as the district never knew before and will never know again, and which lasted all too briefly. By the 1870's the mines were collapsing everywhere, victims of cheap imported Australian and Malaysian tin. Wrote one observer in 1879: "Nothing is plainer than that we are passing through a period of transition at St. Ives. Why, a miner going over the road now is almost as rare a sight as a kilted Highlander, though we used to meet them every day, going to and coming from bal, in droves. The ruins of mines in full work and paying dividends a few years ago, everywhere meet the eye, looking not as picturesquely but quite as forlorn, as the ruins of ancient cities. The old stamps, whose rattling sound was always dinning in your ears, morning, noon and night, are now as silent as the grave. Mines and miners have passed away like a dream, and the next generation will be asking the meaning of all those ruined houses and those monster piles of rubbish."[5]

By about 1890 the industry was virtually dead in this area. Around 1905, however, an improved price for tin, and the introduction of electric pumping equipment led to a revival, several mines being restarted, but the only ones to make any appreciable returns were Trenwith (of radium) and St. Ives Consols and Giew (of tin.) Of these, only Giew survived the Great War; but it succumbed to economic and labour difficulties in 1922, and with its closing mining at St. Ives came to an end. Water wheels continued to be used to work small, eight-head sets of stamps in the deep valleys surrounding the Penwith granite. Many of these worked for years after the mines had fallen silent, crushing horse-drawn cart loads of tin ore which out-of-work miners laboriously hand-sorted from the great heaps of mine waste which scarred the landscape.

The levels and stopes from whence this material had come filled with water, and ladders and pitwork left in place may still be seen leading down into the crystal clear, blue-green depths of the silent flooded shafts. In place of the rhythmic thump of the hammers on iron drills swung by miners, many of whom ended their days in overseas graveyards, only the drip of water can be heard in the long-abandoned workings. Whether there will ever be a second resurgence must remain a matter for conjecture.

1. "Killas" is a general Cornish term for thermally altered clayey rocks.
2. Cann, F.C. The Mines, Lodes and Minerals of the Stennack Valley, St. Ives. *Trans. Corn. Inst. Min. Eng.*, vol. x, 1917.
3. Pool, P.A.S. *The Place-Names of West Penwith,* 1973.
4. *Jour. Roy. Inst. of Corn.,* vol. iv.
5. *Cornish Telegraph* May 13, 1879.

PRINCIPAL SOURCES

Cann, F.C. 1917. The Mines, Lodes and Minerals of the Stennack Valley, St. Ives. (Trans. Corn. Inst. Min. Eng., vol. x.)
Collins, J.H. 1912. Observations on the West of England Mining Region. (Trans. Roy. Geol. Soc. Corn., xiv.)
Dines, H.G., 1956. The Metalliferous Mining Region of South-West England.
Henwood, W.J. 1843. On the Metalliferous Deposits of Cornwall and Devon. (Trans. Roy. Geol. Soc. Corn., v.)
Henwood, W.J. 1865. Observations on Providence Mines. (Trans. Roy. Geol. Soc. Corn., vii.)
Hunt, R. 1884. British Mining.
Jenkin, A.K. Hamilton, 1961. Mines and Miners of Cornwall, I. Around St. Ives
MacAlister, D.A. 1907. The Geology of the Land's End District.
Spargo, T. 1865. The Mines of Cornwall and Devon.
Williams, J. 1861, 1870. Devon and Cornwall Mining Directory.

Newspapers:
Sherborne Mercury; Royal Cornwall Gazette; West Briton; Cornubian; Penzance Gazette; Penzance Journal; Cornish Telegraph; Cornishman; St. Ives Weekly Summary; Western Echo; St. Ives Times.

ABBREVIATIONS

MSM	Mining and Smelting Magazine
MJ	Mining Journal
MW	Mining World
PRO	Public Record Office
SCR,CRO	Stannary Court Records, County Record Office, Truro
J.B.	Justin Brooke
A.K.H.J.	Dr. A.K. Hamilton Jenkin
J.H.T.	John H. Trounson

BALNOON

In the upper part of the valley running between Trink and Worvas hills there formerly existed a little mining village, complete with chapel, known as Balnoon. Some remains of the mine from which it took its name may still be seen just to the north of the main road near this spot; it closely adjoins Worvas Downs mine lying still further to the north. Balnoon — spelt as Ballanoone in 1682, meaning "mine on the down" — is a very ancient working, and must have been active when the Cornish language was still spoken in the area. The lodes, which have been variously described as resembling carbonas, or as tin floors (Hawkins, 1822) lay in decomposed granite having a very soft texture; as a result, the levels were always liable to collapse, sometimes with fatal results, even when supported by the strongest timbers and with pillars of pure tin reluctantly left at intervals to hold up the hanging wall. Borlase mentioned such an accident in 1758 (in his *Natural History of Cornwall*) the ground having run in from surface in a large circle, burying all the men working both above and below. Traditions of this disaster lingered on long after Borlase's time. It is said that two miners who were "spalling" tin stuff on the floors, became alarmed at the appearance of a crack in the ground, and informed the captain; but he laughed at their fears, and stamped around on the crack to prove that the ground was safe. However, the floors immediately after gave way, carrying the two miners to their deaths, but the captain jumped clear. A huge pit, about an acre in extent, with cliff-like walls in some parts, composed of a "trawny" china-clay like material, still marks the scene of the tragedy. The bodies of the two men were never found, and they still lie buried here in their vast and extraordinary tomb.[1]

The tin at Balnoon was noted for its richness; and in 1828 a lode was discovered worth from 20s.-30s. per barrow.[2] The value of the mine was further illustrated when 4/114th shares in it were auctioned at the Golden Lion Inn, Penzance, two years later. The advertisement of the sale stated that it had been for many years a very profitable speculation, and was considered by all competent judges to be the most productive in the neighbourhood. "At the last quarterly account nearly £1,000 (the profits of the previous three months only) were divided amongst the Adventurers, and a much greater sum than this is expected to be divided at the next account."[3] These excellent financial results had, however, been causing considerable legal difficulties. In January of that year Lord de Dunstanville and Basset, and Sir Charles Lemon, on behalf of themselves and fellow bounders in the mine brought a case in the Stannaries Court against William West, Robert Bennet and other adventurers, concerning the latters' title to the lease. It appeared that, prior to July 1825 West had agreed for a sett of Balnoon, which the plaintiffs now claimed was an agreement only, but which the defendants maintained was a lease. By virtue of the right derived from this instrument West and his partners worked the mine and in due course raised considerable quantities of ore. Observing this success, Mr. Praed (presumably of Trevetho) laid claim to the whole bounds of the mine, whereupon the dues were withheld by the adventurers from de Dunstanville and his fellow bounders, who then instituted this suit against them for payment. The question at issue therefore was, whether a tenant could impeach the title, however defective, of the persons granting him a sett. The Vice-Warden said the point was one of great importance to the County. The mine's account books showed that the dues accruing to the plaintiffs on ore raised in Balnoon bounds—the part of Balnoon Mine that was in dispute — amounted to £187 up to May 1829, for which sum judgement was given to the plaintiffs, subject to the objections raised as to the validity of the instrument produced. Lord de Dunstanville and most of the other plaintiffs, recognising that the adventurers had become involved in this action through no fault of their own, said they would not demand the forfeiture of the sett, except as a matter of form; but one of the bounders, called Ellis, showing remarkable vindictiveness, said he would certainly press for the forfeiture. Following an adjournment, the Vice-Warden confirmed his award, observing that the instrument involved in the case was a sett or licence to search for tin over a tin bounds, reserving a certain part of the tin stuff for toll, and from which eventually might be nothing if no tin were found. This was usually called a tin sett; and from the time of William III to the 5th George IV proceedings relating thereto in the Stannaries Courts had been expressly exempted from Stamp Duties. From this circumstance, popular opinion prevailed in Cornwall that all the setts and papers relating to tin or tin mines or streams were exempt from those duties, and very few setts were ever stamped.[4] From this observation, it would seem that the instrument involved in this case had not been stamped, so permitting its validity to be questioned.

An unfortunate accident occurred in May 1836, a timberman named Colan Williams being killed when a plank placed across an old shaft, on which he was standing, gave way, precipitating him to a depth of 13 fms.[5] Two others were seriously injured in February 1839 by the premature explosion of a charge of powder.[6]

This working came to an end in May 1840 when all the mine's materials were offered for sale, including a 30″ pumping engine; two capstans and shears; a 24″ steam stamping engine, for 24 heads, with boiler, axles, frames and lifters; and two horse whims, with kibbles and chains.[7] The mine was active again in 1847, when a good lode of tin was reported to have been discovered.[8] In February 1853 the enterprise, then operating under the name of "Balnoon Consols," was said to look remarkably well; they had 16 men at work on the tin, which continued as rich as ever. In January they had sold £321 worth which had been stamped in one month by nine heads, half of this being profit. They were trying to obtain another stamps, which would considerably increase the returns, as the stuff could not be stamped as fast as it could be broken.[9] At the quarterly meeting held on April 8 it was announced that four months' output of tin (15 tons 12 cwt. 1 qr.) had been sold in six parcels at from £63 10s. to £74 per ton for £1,070 19s. 1d., producing a profit of

£365 19s. 2d., or more than ten per cent on the subscribed capital.[10] In January 1856, however, it was announced that operations had been suspended for a few weeks, though it was intended to resume them with great vigour.[10] Regular calls were made during the following year; and the end of the road was reached for Balnoon Consols on March 30 1858, when the adventurers decided to suspend the mine. At the sale, which took place in May, the principal item was the 30″ cylinder pumping engine, 9′ stroke in the cylinder and 8′ stroke in the shaft, with stamps attached, consisting of auxiliary beam, iron axle to lift 24 heads, fly wheel, sweep rod, cranks, and 9 tons boiler.[12] Balnoon had a recorded output of 165 tons of black tin from 1837-9 and 1852-6. (See also under Worvas Downs.)

1. Hunt, Robert, *Popular Romances of the West of England,* 1871
2. *Royal Cornwall Gazette* April 12 1828
3. *Royal Cornwall Gazette* December 25 1828
4. *Royal Cornwall Gazette* January 9 and February 2 1830
5. *Royal Cornwall Gazette* May 20 1836
6. *Royal Cornwall Gazette* February 8 1839
7. *Royal Cornwall Gazette* May 1 1840
8. *Royal Cornwall Gazette* August 27 1847
9. *Cornish Telegraph* February 16 1853
10. *Cornish Telegraph* April 20 1853
11. *Cornish Telegraph* January 9 1856
12. *Cornish Telegraph* April 16 and May 14 1858

BLACK ROCK

In May 1885 when blasting the blue elvan cliffs at the Black Rock, near Lelant Ferry, "for road purposes," a tidy lode of tin was discovered, and specimens were taken for examination.[1] As far as is known, the lode was never worked. The ferry ran from the beach below the railway bridge at the S.E. end of Lelant Towans.

1. *Cornish Telegraph* May 7 and 21 1885

CANON'S TOWN MINE

In August 1847 a valuable tin lode, about 2′ wide, was discovered in Canon's Town Mine, near Treloweth. This, added to others then working in similar strata and running parallel with the adjacent mines would, it was hoped, afford considerable employment for the "vast" mining population of that district. The mine had commenced operations about four months previously.[1]

1. *Royal Cornwall Gazette* August 27 1847

WHEAL CATHERINE

Just at about the time (January 1876) when Wheal Sisters was being created by the amalgamation of Wheals Mary, Margaret and Kitty the *Cornish Telegraph* carried a report of an interesting discovery made in its vicinity. Some water having lodged in a field on the Trembethow Estate, Lelant, a man was sent to cut a drain. Just two or three feet below the surface he came across a well defined tin lode; this was traced for a short distance on either side of the accidental surface cross-cut, and proved to be excellent stuff — worth £1 a sack of 22 gallons as tinstone, with some pieces yielding 60 and 70% tin. Arrangements were made to test this find, which lay close to Wheal Margaret, but Capt. Rosewarne, manager of Wheal Sisters, stopped further exploration pending the outcome of a claim which he made on behalf of his employers. His contention appeared to be that, according to the sett of Wheal Margaret, any ore discovered within 100 fms. of that mine should be worked by the holders of the sett. Others, however, thought that the clause in the lease applied to discoveries made underground in Wheal Margaret, which could be pursued for 100 fms. out of the sett itself as a reward for exertions in finding deposits of ore. "This point is of secondary interest to the public, who are chiefly concerned in the fact that in the days when it was thought the surface of Cornwall had been thoroughly ransacked for the backs of lodes the spade of the trench-digger turns up what may lead to a large mine."

It would appear that Capt. Rosewarne's claim was not sustained, the newly-discovered mine being worked independently under the name of Wheal Catherine. A report issued by the adventurers in February stated that, having driven the end 12 fms. E. to the water level, they had found the lode going down; being about 12′ deep, this could be a valuable and lasting tin discovery, particularly as it improved with depth. "I believe," wrote William Penberthy, "there is a wonderful deposit of tin standing in this ground, which, if explored, will prove a great blessing to this district for the rising generation."[1] In April, the agents stated: "Notwithstanding the rumour that the production of our tin has declined, we are glad to inform the public that we have again sold about 13 cwt. of black tin; and but for the unfavourable weather since our last sale, we could have raised three times the amount. The lode going down still looks well; and if a cross-cut was driven in to take away the water, it would pay well to work at 6s. in the £. We intend dividing the mine into a hundred shares for the purpose of exploring the ground with greater vigour. — William Penberthy and Richard Jacka, Ludgvan, and John Harris, Lelant."[2]

1. *Cornish Telegraph* February 29 1876
2. *Cornish Telegraph* April 25 1876

WHEAL CHANCE, LELANT

On April 8 1840 Christopher Oates, purser of "Wheal Chance Mine, in the Parish of Lelant," published a sternly worded notice to the shareholders, warning them that if they failed to attend a special meeting to be held on the mine on the 22nd "for the purpose of paying all back Costs and future proceedings in working," their shares would be forfeit.[1]

1. *West Briton* April 10 1840

WHEAL CHERRY (NEW TRENCROM, MOUNT LANE MINE)

This sett includes the summit of Trencrom Hill and a portion of the ground worked in Praed Consols; environmental considerations will almost certainly preclude its working ever being resumed! Trencrom lies just within the granite boundary, but the mine extends into the overlying metamorphosed killas on the east.

At a meeting of Wheal Cherry adventurers held on February 3 1858, it was stated that the total expenditure of £2,293 included the purchase and erection of a 24″ pumping engine and a 24″ whim with 16 heads of stamps attached. A call of £2 10s. per share was agreed.[1] This venture seems to have been a disastrous failure; for only seven months later the sett and materials were offered for sale. In the advertisement, the pumping engine was said to have a 7′ stroke in the shaft and 9′ in the cylinder. There were also an eight-arm capstan, with oak axle; 54′ shears; 120 fms. of $7\frac{1}{2}$″ capstan rope (top hemp new); and a horse whim with 10′ cage. One assumes the mine had collapsed for financial reasons before it could be given a fair trial; at all events, it was described as a valuable property, "as from all authenticated reports Wheal Cherry will be a safe and profitable investment." It lay in one of the best tin districts in the county, being adjoined by Wheal Kitty and Wheal Margaret on the west and East Margaret on the east, with Providence and other rich mines not far distant to the north. It possessed all the necessary machinery and materials (nearly new) for efficient development of the mine.[2] The *Mining Journal* of March 24 1860 reported that additional ground had been acquired and the name changed to Praed Consols (*q.v.*). The Wheal Cherry company was liquidated by the Vice Warden's Court between February 1864 and June 1873; there is a file on this at the County Record Office, Truro.

Golden Bank and Wheal Chance United Tin Mining Company,

PENZANCE, CORNWALL.

AT a MEETING of the ADVENTURERS, held in LONDON, on THURSDAY, the 13th of June, 1839, it was, amongst other things,

RESOLVED—That the Shares of the Company be altered from 3,000, at £5 each, to 600, at £25 each; and that the Shares relinguished, and also the Sares which are, or shall become forfeited, being so reduced, be Disposed of, for the benefit of the company, at £3. 10s. per one Six-hundredth Part or Share, and

That the Solicitors of the Company be authorised to take the necessary steps to legalize the forfeiture of all Shares, upon which the Calls due shall not have been paid.

NOTICE is, therefore HEREBY GIVEN, that all Persons claiming an interest in the above Mines, are required, on or before the 5th day of AUGUST, now next ensuing, to signify their intention to the undersigned of continuing their interest, and paying up the Call in arrear, or of discontinuing the same, and that the Adventurers, who shall so continue their interest, may have the old Scrip exchanged for Certificates to be granted according to the regulations of the Trust Deed.

A'BECKET, SON, AND SYMPSON.

Dated 7, Golden-square, London, 11th July, 1839.

At the beginning of the present century the sett was taken up by Messrs. Gerry Brothers, of Lelant. After five years of prospecting they relinquished their interest in 1907 to another group. At this time, considerable activity was reported on the eastern slope of Trencrom Hill. A new shaft was in process of sinking, which had, at a depth of 7 fms., revealed a good E. and W. lode about 2′ wide with a northerly underlie of 18″ to the fathom. It was a strong and capable lode in granite, the average yield being 60 lbs. of black tin to the ton, the highest assay exceeding 100 lbs. There was another known lode running parallel to this, also dipping N.; its average width was about 2½′, and old miners described it as highly prospective. Only one shaft existed on this lode, about 9 fms. deep; they intended to re-open it and explore the ground. A deep adit would also be driven from Mount Croft right through the property to ascertain the lodes and drain the water, which was already hindering operations in the new shaft.[3] Work was still continuing at Wheal Cherry in 1916. Exploratory operations were resumed in a part of the property known as Mount Lane Mine in 1943, but results proved disappointing, and there was no production.

1. *Cornish Telegraph* February 19 1858
2. *Royal Cornwall Gazette* August 18 1858
3. *Western Echo* June 8 1907

COLLURIAN

Collurian Mine lay on the south side of the valley running west from Canon's Town, and worked the same run of lodes as were found in Wheal Merth on the opposite side of the stream.

See also under Ludgvan Wheal Margaret.

WHEAL COMFORT

This mine, at Carbis Bay, was on two occasions involved in amalgamations with its neighbours, in the first (1815) to form "The United Mines of Wheal Comfort, Wheal Speed, Wheal Hazard, and East and West Wheal Crack," and in the second (1832) with the addition of Providence, Wheal Laity and Good Fortune, as the "Providence Mines", *q.v.* Between 1832-4, however, it seems to have retained a semi-autonomous status; and a few entries from its cost book for that period give some idea of the rather limited scale of its operations:

"Building Changing House, 3s. 6d. (It must have been a doll's house!) Spilling through addle (attle, waste rock) in adit. Colering adit shaft. Ann Trevorrow drawing potatoes, 8d. (Doubtless grown on land belonging to the mine.) Heaving up whim and spanbeam. Building Moorhouse. Washeing & Mending Agents' clothes, 11 months, 6s. Putting in Bob stand, assisting to put up horse engine, etc. February 1833: alowed the men on putting the engine to work. Spilling Meddle adit toward Wheal Laity. Paid for a pair of Under ground Shooes, 6s. 6d. Mending, 1s. To Carpenters on putting Stamps to work, 7s. Sawing Oak for the Stamps, £1. Paid Carriers and Sack washers. Putting on Roas (Rose) Lift. Cutting ground for Cistren. Putting in bearers. December 1833: Poors and High way Rate on Stamps, 12s. Putting in the pressure engine.''

On September 10 1834 Joseph Vivian wrote a report on the mine, in which he recommended the adventurers to erect a steam engine, so enabling them to extend their limits by securing East Providence and Wheal Speed setts, then idle, which were closely connected and on the same lodes as Providence and Laity. At Wheal Comfort the water was in, but the recent showers would give sufficient power to clear the workings in a few days and keep them so for about six months, using the existing water engine. He advised pushing on the 30 fm. level S. to cut Laity lodes, and clearing Providence adit, which could be done for a few pounds.[1]

1. *Letter Book, C.R.O., Truro*

WHEAL CUPID

This copper mine (also known as Cubert) lies in the little wood which extends northwards from Trevetho Farm towards Longstone cemetery. It is interesting to find among the field names of Trevetho ''Burning House'' (for calcining), and among those of the adjoining Trenoweth Farm ''Park Shafters, or Shaftoes'' (shafts.) The late R. Morton Nance conjecturally translated Cupid as ''pit close'' (from *kew pyt,*)[1] which, if correct, effectually dispels any romantic associations it might otherwise have held!

The western extension of Hawke's Point mine, *q.v.,* known as ''Cubitt,'' which may be identified with this sett, was ''knocked'' in 1854; but Wheal Cupid also apparently had an independent existence at one period. In June 1860 it was stated that at a general meeting of the adventurers in Wheal Cupid, the accounts, showing a debit balance of £192 0s. 4d., and the report — of a favourable character — were passed, a call of 2s. per share then being made.[2]

1. In notes appended to G.H. Doble's *Lananta,* 1939
2. *Cornish Telegraph* June 20 1860

WHEAL GIFT

In April 1828 it was announced that a valuable tin lode had been discovered in a mine just set to work adjoining Balnoon, called Wheal Gift, in the parish of Lelant.[1] The mine lay between Balnoon and the Porthia china clay works, and was sunk in the same strata of decomposed granite as those enterprises. Several more lodes were later found, but Wheal Gift never developed into a large mine. In 1864-5 the sett was reworked under the name of South St. Ives, *q.v.*

1. *Royal Cornwall Gazette* April 19 1828

WHEAL GILBERT CONSOLS

This mine, in Lelant, was opened privately by a cost-book company in the spring of 1875, with J.B. Reynolds as purser, Capt. James Pope manager and Capt. Stephen Pope agent. In May a discovery of tin was made which, according to a correspondent, promised to be "of magnitude." In June the manager reported the lode in adit level as 9″ wide and producing rich stones of tin. In a rise in the back of the adit E. of shaft the lode was 15″ wide and worth £8 per fm.

A meeting of Old Tincroft Consols held in November resolved to add Wheal Gilbert sett to their own, which they believed would be a considerable acquisition. In the autumn of 1876 the New Tincroft United Mining Company, Limited, was registered in Truro to work the joint property.[1]

The name "Gilbert" appears to have been given in compliment to that family, whose most distinguished member was the historian Davies Gilbert, FRS, of Tredrea, St. Erth. They possessed a manor extending over five parishes, of which the "vokeland" was "Amellibrea" in Towednack.[2]

1. MW 1875 (22.5, 5.6, 23.10, 13.11), 1876 (1.4)
   Hunt's Min. Stats. 1875
2. Gilbert, Davies, *Parochial History of Cornwall,* iv, 1838

GOLDEN BANK AND WHEAL CHANCE

The site of the Wheal Chance section of this attractively named mine has been identified by Dr. A. K. H. Jenkin as immediately east of Ashtown and due north of Cucurrian Mill, on the Nancledra stream, but Golden Bank has not been precisely located.[1] The mine was active in the period 1837-45. In 1839 the "Golden Bank and Wheal Chance United Tin Mining Company," of Penzance, announced that a meeting of the adventurers held in London on June 13th had resolved that the shares of the company should be altered from 3,000 at £5 each to 600 at £25 each; and that relinquished and forfeited shares, being so reduced, should be disposed of at £3 10s. per one six-hundredth part. Adventurers continuing their interest could have their old scrip exchanged for certificates to be granted according to the regulations of the trust deed.[2] This affords an interesting example of a scrip company changing over to the more conventional cost-book system.

1. *Mines and Miners of Cornwall,* Vol. I, 1961
2. *West Briton* July 19 1839

WHEAL GRACE

This mine lay in the tenement of Carninney, Lelant, and was making sales of black tin and occasionally copper in 1756-68. In 1832 it was consolidated with a number of its neighbours to form the Providence Mines.[1]

1. London & West Country Chamber of Mines Records 1904-7, p. 192; Collins, J.H., 1912, p. 158. (Note: J.H. Collins was Editor of the Records of the L&WCCM.)
A.K.H. Jenkin, *Mines & Miners of Cornwall,* pt. 1, p. 30

HAWKE'S POINT MINE (WHEAL FANNY ADELA)

The bold headland which divides Carbis Bay from Porthkidney Beach is known as Carrack Gladden; but its more popular name of Hawke's Point properly belongs to the tiny promontory on its southern flank where a flight of rough-hewn steps leads down to the shore by an old mine adit in the cliff.[1] This adit, and other adjacent workings, formed part of the old Hawke's Point Mine, which was active at various periods between the 1840's and '80's. It also possessed an inland extension known as Cubitt; this presumably was Wheal Cupid, *q.v.*, which lay in the wood S. of Longstone cemetery. In 1849 and 1851-3 Hawke's Point is said to have sold 706 tons of copper ore (31 tons metal) for £2,363.[2] In 1852 the mine was reported to be held in 512 shares, and was making calls.[3]

In February 1854 the adventurers decided to abandon the western or Cubitt part, and as a consequence all the machinery and materials thereon were offered for sale by auction. These included a 24″ cylinder engine, 7′ stroke in the cylinder and 6′ in the shaft, with cistern and condensing work, complete; 8 tons boiler; balance bob; capstan and shears, nearly new; 80 fms. of 9″ capstan rope; horse whim; and a "horse engine." Particulars could be obtained from Mr. W. Richards, the purser.[4]

The cliff section of the mine appears to have been "knocked" soon after; but during the mid-1860's it was resumed under the charming name of "Wheal Fanny Adela." This seems to have been bestowed in compliment to Miss Fanny Adela Wilby, daughter of Col. W. Wilby, commanding 1st. Batt. King's Own Regiment, who in March 1865 became the bride of William Backwell Tyringham, Esq., of Tyringham, Bucks., and Trevetho, Cornwall, the marriage being celebrated at Trevetho House, Lelant, "with great rejoicings." The Tyringhams (Praeds), it need hardly be added, held many of the mineral rights in the district. The 1870 *Devon and Cornwall Mining Directory* states that the mine was held in 2,700 shares, its produce being tin, copper and lead; the purser was A.H.D. Vivian, Camborne; agent, H. Stevens; and the engineer W. Bennetts; the depth was 25 fms., five persons being employed.

Wheal Fanny Adela stopped during the following year; but when the St. Ives branch railway was being constructed in 1874-77 the miners employed in excavating the vast Carrack Gladden cutting intersected some of the Hawke's Point lodes, and were with difficulty restrained from resuming their old calling!

In July 1883 Mr. N.T. Ashton, chemist and druggist of St. Ives, began mining operations on the headland with the object of producing

Hawke's Point Mine,

IN LELANT.

ENGINE AND MATERIALS FOR SALE.

AN AUCTION will be held on the above mine on Tuesday, the 28th of February instant, at 10 o'clock in the morning, for selling the whole of the

MACHINERY

AND MATERIALS

On the Cubitt part of the above mine, which has been discontinued and which comprises

A 24-inch Cylinder Engine, 7 feet stroke in the cylinder and 6 in the Shaft with cistern and condensing work complete; a Boiler 8 tons, with steam and feed pipes; Balance Bob; Capstan and Shears nearly new, with Sheave; 80 fms. of 9-in. capstan rope; 10 9-ft. 10-in. pumps; 11 9-ft. 9-in. pumps; 4 9-ft. 7-in pumps; 2 3-ft. 8-in. pumps; 79 feet 6-inch, and one 7 feet 7-inch, pumps, 1 3-ft. 9-in. H piece; 1 3-ft. 9-inch top door piece; 1 4-ft. 9-in. windbore; 1 10-ft. 7-inch working, 1 9-ft. 8-in., 1 6-ft. 8-in., 1 2-ft. 7-inch, and 1 6-ft. 8-in. clack door pieces; 1 4-ft 7-in. and 1 9-ft. 7-in. windbores; 1 6-ft. 7-inch bucket door piece; 1 7½ 4½ working; 1 4 feet 6 inch windbore; 1 2 feet 7 inch clack doorpiece; 2 2 feet 8 in. matching piece; 1 9 feet 8 inch and 1 9 feet 6 inch plunger poles with stuffing box and gland; 25 fathoms of 7 inch main rod; 5 fathoms of 6 inch rod; 6 fms. of 1¼ and 1¼ bucket rods; 1 pair of 8 inch, 1 of 7 inch, and 1 of 6 inch prongs; 1 horse whim; shaft tackle complete; 2 4 feet sheaves, light; 1 4 feet do., heavy, with plummer block and brasses; 1 2 feet sheave; horse whim chain; 2 kebbles; 1 sett of shaft rollers; 1 2 feet flat sheave with plummer block and brasses; 3 setts of strapping plates with belts and nuts 1 horse engine; iron work; a lot of ¾ inch chain; a 40 inch smith's bellows, very good; an anvil and vice; smith's tools; screw tools; screw stocks; miner's tools; sundry lots of new and old iron; 1 large beam scales and stand, and 1 small one; 100 fms. of 5 inch launders; 10 fm. of air pipes; 2 cisterns; 4 jigging hutches; carpenter's bench; and a variety of other articles.

For further particulars apply to Mr. W. RICHARDS, the Purser, or at the offices of

Messrs. RODD, DARKE, AND CORNISH,

Solicitors, Penzance.

Dated 7th February, 1854.

cobalt and nickel, as well as copper.[5] He persevered with the enterprise for nineteen years; and with his brother Edward (who resided at Hawke's Point) and Edward's wife, Elizabeth, spent the whole of many a night assaying and refining ores in a furnace house on the cliff top.[6] For a time, employment was provided for several workmen, but the mine proved a profitless speculation and was eventually closed. Edward Ashton was one of the earliest St. Ives photographers, and with his camera recorded many fascinating glimpses of that town around the turn of the century. His wife, best remembered as ''Grannie'' Ashton, was a remarkable character. She ran the famous picnic grounds at Hawke's Point for many years, and possessed strange gifts as a water diviner and healer.

There was another small mine in the cliff at Grotto Point, incorrectly marked ''Hawk's Point'' on the O.S. map, lying about a quarter of a mile S.E. of Carrack Gladden at the opposite end of the Nut Grove; it appears to have been little more than a trial. A short distance inland, at Gonwin Farm, there are traces of early mine workings; and an old St. Ives miner once told the writer that in a nearby field he had discovered with the dowsing rod what he believed to be an extremely rich lode, probably of copper.

1. Noall, Cyril, *Beloved St. Ives,* 1957
2. Jenkin, A.K.H., *Cornish Mines and Miners,* i, 1961
3. *Cornish Telegraph* November 23 1852
4. *Cornish Telegraph* February 1854
5. *Cornishman* and *Cornish Telegraph* July 26 1883
6. *Western Echo* May 19 1928

WHEAL HOPE, LELANT

The *Penzance Gazette* of July 9 1845 announced the sale by auction of ''all those valuable Tin and Copper Mines, called Wheal Hope, situate in the parish of Uny Lelant,'' held by the adventurers under setts, twenty years of which remained unexpired. The materials included a 24″ engine with six tons boiler; ''the first piece of the Main Rod'' — these items, being very sturdy, and consequently expensive to replace, were often specially mentioned in engine sales — horse whim, with shaft tackle and two 4′ shieves; about 30 fms. 7/16″ horse whim chain; 5 cwt. of gunpowder; burning house; counting house furniture; tools; and ''Buck'' — presumably an appliance for breaking or ''bucking'' copper ore.

The location of this mine is not known with absolute certainty; but when 2-85th shares in Wheal Hope were offered for sale in December 1844, it was described as being ''near Treloweth, in Lelant.'' It therefore seems possible that this was the original name of Treloweth mine (*q.v.*) which adjoined St. Erth railway station.

WHEAL KITTY (POLPEOR)

This is the most easterly of the Wheal Sisters trio, its workings lying adjacent to the hamlet of Polpeor. It may originally have been known by a different name. In the will of John Edwards, of Lelant, dated April 27 1742, he mentions his estate in Parkandreas, Ye Tye Down, with Little Moor, Gonew, the tenement of Enis, otherwise Ninis; and his "one-third adventure in a pitch called Ye Providence in Powlpear."

In March 1811 a pare of men went down into some old workings at Wheal Kitty to clear away the deads, but neglected to take with them the timber allotted for supporting the ground. As a result, a part of one of the old shafts gave way and killed three of them, their bodies not being recovered till the following day. One, who belonged to Col. Halse's St. Ives Volunteers, was buried with military honours — "and such an immense concourse of people attended as was never before seen; the church was not only crowded, but the churchyard was also full."[1]

Wheal Kitty

Wheal Kitty's most important period of working commenced around 1846. An unfortunate accident occurred at the mine in December 1853. William Roberts, a young man of 18, had been working in the 25 fm. level, and came up to the 16 fm. level for a hand saw; in attempting to cross the shaft on a plank he slipped and fell to the 100 fm. level. "When found, his body was literally smashed to atoms."[2]

In 1855 the mine was 120 fms. below adit (27 fms.) For some years the adventurers had had to meet a series of calls, but from the mid fifties onwards modest but regular profits were made. At a typical meeting, held on December 19 1855 a dividend of £512 (£2 per 256th share) was declared.[3] By 1864 a depth of 163 fms. below adit had been attained; the machinery comprised two pumping engines of 33″ and 28″, and one 24″ stamping and winding engine; 147 persons were employed. It was stated in 1869 that Wheal Kitty had yielded metal worth £275,000 and divided profits of £57,000.[4]

A compact lode was being worked in the north adit level in October 1872, composed of mundic, blende and spots of copper ore, with a small percentage of tin. Unfortunately, before this discovery could be fully exploited, Wheal Kitty succumbed to the mining depression of the following year. However, the mine bore such a good reputation that when offered for sale as a going concern a new consortium of adventurers acquired the property and continued operations without even stopping the engines. At a meeting held in the Western Hotel, Penzance, during October, the name of the speculation was changed to "Polpeor," which was then divided into 1,000 shares of £3 2s. 6d. each. These were allotted to Messrs. T.S. Bolitho & Sons, Messrs. Harvey & Co., Mr. J.B. Coulson, Capt. Richard Perry of Chyangweal, and Capt. William Rosewarne of Leedstown. An excellent tin lode was reported to be opening at the 150 fm. level, whilst the 60 fm. level also looked exceedingly well.[5] Polpeor had but a very short independent existence, as drainage difficulties during the rainy winter of 1874-5 caused it to be amalgamated with its neighbours, Margaret, Mary and Trencrom, under the name of Wheal Sisters, *q.v.*

1. *Sherborne Mercury* March 25 1811
2. *Cornish Telegraph* January 4 1854
3. *Cornish Telegraph* January 9 1856
4. *Cornish Telegraph* October 20 1869
5. *Cornish Telegraph* August 20 and October 22 1873

Wheal Kitty

SOUTH WHEAL KITTY

This little mine lay on the south bank of the Canon's Town valley opposite Wheal Merth. In 1861 it was 15 fms. deep and employed twenty persons. Some prospecting seems to have been carried on between 1900-5, and again later this century, but with disappointing results.

LELANT CONSOLS

This mine lies immediately south of Wheal Margaret, and about half-a-mile east of Nancledra, one of its shafts (Engine) being just a hundred yards south by east of the well-known Cornish cross at Brunnion Carn. Although working on parallel lodes to that mine, it proved to be Margaret's poor relation, the returns being consistently disappointing. Little is known of its early history. In June 1825 its materials were offered for sale by auction, these including "an excellent Steam Engine, Cylinder 15 Inches Diameter and 8 ft. Stroke, with Cast

Iron Beam, and high Pressure Boiler; 1 Steam Whim Axle Tree, 12 ft. long, 2 ft. square, with cranks to suit; 1 Horse Whim, Whim Kibbles," etc.[1] All these items were described as "nearly new, and well worth the attention of Miners in general," from which it may be inferred that this marked the end of a brief and unsuccessful phase of working

Its materials were again advertised for sale in the *Royal Cornwall Gazette* of October 13 1832, being then described as a steam engine, 15½ inch cylinder, with cast iron bob, etc., complete; ten 6 inch pumps; seven 7 inch ditto; and "70 fathoms of Flat Rods, two by one, of the best Colebrookdale Iron." The advertisement continued: "The late Adventurers in Lelant Consols Mine, having no intention, at present, of trying WHEAL KITTY, or the South Lodes, of which both are very promising, and within the power of the Engine, any person wishing to prosecute either or both the lodes, may do so on easy terms, the Machinery, together with all erections being on the spot, will be sold at a reasonable price." Enquiries were to be directed to Francis Soddy, auctioneer, appraiser and mine broker, Lelant.

It was active again in 1838, 20 persons being then employed, but a further sale took place in March 1840, this time of "all those valuable Mines, called or known by the name of The Lelant Consolidated Mines, together with the Materials thereon, situate in the Parish of Uny Lelant . . . adjoining the valuable Mines of Wheal Reeth, Wheal Mary, Wheal Margaret and Tincroft, and not far distant from St. Ives Consols, Reeth Consols, and Balnoon." They were said to have produced large quantities of tin, though only worked on a limited scale. The mines could be viewed by applying to Capt. Roach on the spot, or to the office of the late Thomas Teague, Esq., Redruth.[2] In 1847 an advertisement was issued for an agent, who was expected to reside on or near the mine and devote his whole time to it, working in conjunction with a superintending agent — "Salary, for the present, five guineas a month." At the same time, 5/128th shares in the enterprise were offered for sale.[3]

The quarterly account for March 1851 showed expenditure of £1,552; ores sold £507; a call of £3 being made to meet the deficiency.[4] A new company took over the mine in 1852. Great efforts were made in the following years to bring the enterprise to a dividend-paying state; but perseverance failed to meet its due reward, and the adventurers were faced with a disheartening sequence of calls. At last, in desperation, it was decided to open up a new part of the sett, to the N. and E. of the existing workings, in hopes of obtaining improved results. This itself involved further expenditure. The six months' account published in June 1858 showed a working loss of £386, to meet which, as well as the heavy expenditure on the new mine, a call of £1 was made. A sum of £810 had been spent on the old mine, and £1,015 on the new since October 1857, the total cost of opening the new mine being £3,563.[5] By December this had increased to £4,591.[6]

Unhappily, the adventurers again suffered disappointment. Spargo stated in 1864 that they had displayed great patience, having been paying calls regularly over the past fifteen years. The end was then already in sight, the forty men usually employed having been reduced in number. It possessed a 24″ pumping and a 20″ winding engine, and one water stamps. The workings were 70 fms. under adit (11 fms.). Lelant Consols is in granite, the shafts being Engine, Rodd's and Richard's.

Dines expressed the opinion that the workings of this mine located 100 yards N.E. of Locke Farm may have gone under the name of Trembethow, *q.v.*

1. *Royal Cornwall Gazette* June 18 1825
2. *Royal Cornwall Gazette* March 6 1840
3. *Penzance Gazette* March 10 1847
4. *Royal Cornwall Gazette* March 20 1851
5. *Royal Cornwall Gazette* June 25 1858
6. *Royal Cornwall Gazette* December 8 1858

LELANT TIN BOUNDS

By an indenture dated March 31 1764 drawn between Thomas Kniveton of Lelant and Abel Angove of Illogan, reference was made to an earlier deed of January 1 1742 by which Peter Carveth, late of Nansalverne, assigned a number of West Cornwall bounds, which included the following from Lelant: one pair, Saint Martyn (Martyns) Beam; two pairs, Whele Wallish and Whele Callensoe; one pair, Wheale an Drease an Vor and Whele Calenso; and one pair, Pednamenar (Pednmenmar) (stream bounds.)[1]

1. Senior 73. C. 107. 73 P.R.O. This file is at the Public Records Office, Kew, which comes under the name of the Master in Chancery in whose presence the case was heard. Abel Angove of Illogan was either bankrupted or in financial straits, and borrowed money on the security of his shares in various tin bounds. (Per Justin Brooke.)

LELANT TIN STREAMS AND CLAY WORKS

It is recorded that in ancient times ships sailed up to St. Erth bridge from the sea through Hayle Estuary, but the channel eventually became choked by refuse discharged from mines higher up the valley. Inevitably, much fine tin was washed down with the tailings, forming worthwhile exploitable deposits. Several references occur to tin streaming, or, more correctly, tin recovery, at Lelant. Thus, in 1873, Capt. Edward Winnan, manager of St. Erth Tin Stream, was reported to have sold, in a period of two months, two tons of tin at a profit of £20, and hoped to be equally successful with the Mill Hill stream works in the parish of Lelant.[1] In July 1883 Lelant Tin Stream Works were offered for sale by William Morley; whilst in March 1887 the high price of tin induced a Mr. Stevens to resume the working of the tin stream at Lower Lelant which had been given up some years previously. In 1953 Mr. Bernard James told Mr. Hamilton Jenkin that in 1898 as a boy of fifteen he had been employed on a stream works extracting slime tin from the mud between Trendreath House and Lelant Station. They had 120 frames and two trams bringing up 20 loads a day to the strakes. The tin lay from one to two feet deep only, superimposed on the sea sand. The works closed down when they were getting only £30 a ton for black tin. The dressing water came from the stream which crosses the main road by the chapel, whose source is Wheal Cupid adit. (Wheal Cupid, *q.v.*, lay in Cupid Wood adjoining the North lode of Trevetho estate.)

The ground within the wood at the foot of the hill descending from Lelant Hotel to the railway station, which has the appearance of being mined, was formerly worked for moulding sand — presumably by the Hayle or Copperhouse foundries. A lode crosses the hill diagonally to the road, but when tried by James was found to contain no tin.[3]

From a site near Lelant about 350 tons of clay, derived from decomposed schistus, were annually exported from Hayle to Swansea for the smelting furnaces during the early 19th century.[4]

1. *Cornish Telegraph* May 14 1873
2. *Cornish Telegraph* March 24 1887
3. Hamilton Jenkin Coll., Redruth Library
4. *Transactions of the Royal Geological Society of Cornwall,* vol. i., p. 233 (1818); vol. 3, p. 360 (1828)

WHEAL LOCKE: LOCKE, CHYPONS, AMALEBRA, LITTLE AND BARKLE'S STAMPS

In the valley below Nancledra a little mine called Wheal Locke began operations in 1892. At the close of 1893, whilst sinking a shaft to meet an adit driven at a depth of 10 fms., a lode was cut varying from 3′-4′ in width, producing an average of 2 cwt. of tin to the ton of stuff, with some stones yielding as much as 5 cwt., or 25%. The lode was opened on for 20 fms. in length, and maintained its rich character throughout. As a result, there was a rush from speculators anxious to join the syndicate working the property, which was hoped to provide much additional work for miners who for many years past had found little employment.[1]

Much earlier than this, a water stamps had existed at Locke. An auction announced to be held there on July 22 1808 included a grist mill, two stamping mills with floors and other appurtenances, and a dwelling house occupied by Lewis Charles Daubuz and Henry Thomas.[2]

A disused set of water stamps still survives at Locke. Altogehter, no less than five sets of stamps were once to be found within a distance of a mile and a half at Nancledra Valley. A detailed account of these was given by Andrew Berryman in the Trevithick Society's Newsletter (No. 26, August, 1979). Chypons stamps (4 heads) worked on material from Wheal Kitty burrows. Amalebra (8 heads) stamped tin stuff from Cripple's Ease and a part of Wheal Reeth. Little stamps (4 wood lifters) processed stuff from Tincroft and Carne burrows. Locke, which ceased work around 1942-4, stamped nine or ten cart loads of dump material daily from Wheal Margaret. Barkle's, consisting of two sets of stamps 500 yards apart, was supplied with tin stuff from Wheal Reeth. All these stamps, together with the grist mill at Nancledra, were driven by the

River Lydd, which rises on Amalveor Downs and flows into the sea at Marazion.

1. *Cornish Telegraph* July 3 1894
2. *Royal Cornwall Gazette* July 9 1808

WHEAL LUCY (RIVIERE OR TOWANS MINE): WEST WHEAL LUCY (WEST WHEAL TOWAN, LELANT WHEAL TOWAN)

The south eastern extremity of Porthkidney Beach, Lelant, is bounded by Chapel Angier Point where, in medieval times, a lighthouse was maintained for the guidance of ships frequenting Hayle River. From this headland a stretch of mineralised ground extends southwards for some distance along the course of the estuary, the lodes passing inland under the Towans and the church and village of Lelant. Various small workings were carried out on these lodes in quite early times, the most important being centred on Chapel Angier Point, on either flank of which adits are still visible in the cliff. At the beginning of last century this mine went by the name of West Wheal Towan, but in 1850 was reopened as Lelant Wheal Towan.

A correspondent of the *Mining Journal* stated at that time that about 140 years earlier (*c.* 1710) the vicar of the parish had received large sums annually as dues from a portion of the limits which was then the glebe lands. About 1820 a horse engine had been put up on one of the south lodes and some very rich tin raised, as well as quantities of copper, with the assistance of a small water wheel. This proved insufficient, and the shortage of capital led to the mine's closure.

In 1850 the newly reopened Lelant Towans was said to be held on a 21 year lease at 1-18th dues. It adjoined Hawke's Point Mine, and it was proposed to allow the adventurers in that concern to apply for shares in the present company, any balance remaining being "appropriated," i.e., offered for public subscription. Six of the eight lodes had been worked, some at a very ancient date, but the present operations were confined to clearing an adit taken up at high water mark near the ferry, and believed to be driven on two lodes. The old burrows were covered with sand, and in clearing sand from the adit tail tin had been found. There was also a rich copper lode in the bottom of the mine at a depth of 15 or 20 fms. from surface.[1]

Another correspondent reported in February 1856 that about £500 had been expended, and it was expected that the outlay of a further £1,000 or £1,500 would "place the mine in a promising and permanent state." In 1850 it had been in 512 shares; a 10s. call had been made on these. By 1856 they had been increased to 1,024 (10s. paid), 500 of which were held in Cornwall.[1]

This company went out of existence in 1867; but in 1872 the mine was again revived as West Wheal Lucy. This name originated from Wheal Lucy, which was then active on the Hayle bank of the estuary.

The prospectus of the Riviere or Towans Mine had been issued under the name of Wheal Lucy in March 1871 from St. Michael's House, Cornhill, London; and a cost-book company was formed the following month in 1,000 shares, Mr. Jehu Hitchins being secretary. Capt. James Pope, of Redruth, in an inspection report of the sett, stated:

"This sett is situated in the parish of Phillack (close to Hayle Quays) and is of considerable extent, being about three-quarters of a mile long by half-a-mile wide. It lies to the east of Wheal Mary, Wheal Kitty, Wheal Reeth, Trencrom and Trevarrack Mines, and is traversed by the same run of lodes that has been so productive in those mines. The celebrated Great Wheal Alfred and Mellanear cross-courses which have made such rich deposits of mineral from the north to the south cross the sett, and the strata are of the same congenial character as in the whole of the productive mines in this district. The sett is traversed by several lodes and carbonas of great promise. The surface workings of the old tinners are very extensive on these lodes, and on a carbona a shaft has been sunk four fathoms below the adit, from which, by the aid of a hand-lift, large quantities of tin-stone, some of very rich quality, have been raised and paid handsomely, although at that time tin was only £40 to £50 a ton. In the bottom of this shaft there still remains a first-rate course of tin.

"When the old tinners by these surface workings found such good lodes they commenced driving an adit from the sea level to intersect and unwater them. This adit was driven 70 fathoms, but the capital failing it was abandoned when within 30 fathoms of the main tin lode, wherein the old workers had, according to report, left a good course of tin standing. There are thus two good courses of tin known to be present and easy to get at. I beg to say that I have inspected from time to time almost every mine in Cornwall and Devon and on the Continent, and in all my experience I have never seen a more promising mining property than this. I consider it one of the best mining setts now lying idle in Cornwall."

Work began at Wheal Lucy in August 1871, an engine house, account house, smiths' and carpenters' shops being erected at surface, whilst underground, four shafts were cut down and secured and adits and cross-cuts driven. The engine starting ceremony took place in February 1872 in the presence of a large number of people, the sinking of Engine shaft being thereupon resumed on a good lode. The sixty persons employed on the mine were "hospitably regaled" by the adventurers on setting this engine to work.

Meanwhile, on the western bank of the river rather more limited activity was in evidence at West Wheal Lucy. This sett was said to be very extensive, being nearly 700 fms. in length and 350 fms. in width. It lay on the same run of lodes as Wheal Lucy; there were several of these, running E. and W., intersected by caunter lodes and cross-courses. During previous workings operations had been carried out on five of these lodes to a limited extent, but in each case sufficiently to show their productiveness. Leading agents believed the mine worthy of a vigorous trial, and it was also held in high repute by old miners who had been employed there many years before. An old shaft on one of the south lodes, in the bottom of which there was a good lode of tin, had been cleared to 9 fms. below adit, which was also being cleared, together with a second adit on another south lode. The mine was managed by a London company, of which, as in the case of Wheal Lucy, Mr. Jehu Hitchins was secretary.[3]

In August, at Wheal Lucy (Phillack) the pneumatic stamps of Messrs. Harvey & Co. were performing very satisfactorily, saving two-thirds the fuel required for conventional stamps, and effecting a better separation of tin, more of which was retained at the head of the strips and far less going off in the slimes. A trial conducted by Messrs. Eustice & Son showed that about ten tons per head were stamped in 24 hours, the stuff being equal in hardness to the average of the county. Each head, when new, without lifter, weighed 84 lbs. The lode in the 10 fm. level S. was worth £30 per fm.; drivage here would have been further advanced but for the breaking of the engine crank. The tinstuff broken at East shaft was of moderate quality.[2] During the following month, Capt. W. Harris, of Wheal Lucy, was appointed agent at West Wheal Lucy. By October, the Wheal Lucy dressing floors extension had been nearly completed. Soon after this, difficulties were caused at West Wheal Lucy by a failure of the boiler on the pumping engine; this was repaired and the engine set to work again in early November. The water, meanwhile, had risen in the mine, and was being forked slowly; drivings at the bottom of the shaft would be resumed as soon as possible. The shaft on North lode was down to water, in consequence of which sinking there had been suspended.[3] At Wheal Lucy they had found a carbona; but the breaking of tin here was suspended in December. However, they were driving eastward in the direction of the best tin ground, where an improvement was shortly expected.[4]

In January 1873 fair progress was reported at the western mine in cutting down the shaft, the lode there yielding good stones of copper ore. There was still better news in May; Watson's shaft then sinking on Hitchins's lode, was yielding rich work for tin, the lode being 8′ wide and well defined.[5] In June the lode was described as large and masterly, with fine rocks of tin, Capt. Harris stating that he had never seen so fine a lode at that depth, and it continued to improve as they went down. However, at Wheal Lucy (Phillack) affairs were looking less healthy, the adventurers, meeting in London, being faced with a heavy debit balance and a call of 6s. per share. The chairman (Peter Watson) appealed to Capt. Harris to thoroughly test the points he had in hand.[6] The end came for Wheal Lucy in September. Reporting this event, the *Mining World* stated that the enterprise had been worked since 1871 with hardly a gleam of hope to enliven the dreary path towards liquidation. The agents' reports had been encouraging — very encouraging — but they had not been followed up by any practical result. "Capt. Harris mentioned points which still remained to be proved, but the voice of the charmer was resisted, and the shareholders, like Rachel of old, refused to be comforted. Capt. Harris holds 100 shares in the mine, and his offer to remain without salary for three months must be taken as evidence of his faith in the future of the mine, but after having spent £10,000 on it the shareholders may be excused for declining to proceed with the work.'' It was thought that the sale of the machinery (which had cost £5,000) would cover existing liabilities.

Wheal Lucy, Hayle Towans (C.C.L.)
Wheal Lucy, on Hayle Towans, whose adit opens at the SW end of the Black Cliff. It produced tin in the 1870's and '90's.

Work continued at West Wheal Lucy for a little longer. In December, shaft sinking was resumed by two men and a boy to intersect Hitchins' lode. They would go as deep as they could with water, and then cross-cut north and south to prove the extensive old men's workings.[7] The mine seems to have been knocked soon afterwards. A last echo of this interesting little venture was heard in 1876, when John Hichens **(sic)** of London, and G. H. Eustice, jun., of Hayle, were summoned under the Metalliferous Mines Registration Act, 1872, as owners and lessees of West Wheal Lucy, in Lelant, for having permitted two shafts to remain unsafe and unfenced after written notice had been served on them by Dr. C. Le Neve Foster, inspector of mines. Woodward's shaft had been covered by $1\frac{1}{2}$" thick boards, but was otherwise unprotected, as required by the Act. Dr. Foster considered the erection of a hedge the safest means of securing a shaft. Thomas Lang, railway contractor, who was then building the St. Ives branch line, deposed he had frequently passed by the shaft and found it unsafe. The footpath was only 30′ away, and one or two boards were often missing. Eustice said he had ceased to be connected with the mine in April 1874. He had received Dr. Foster's notices, and gave due notice himself to the right persons. Just before he left there were six shafts requiring attention. He had experienced great difficulty in getting men to go down the shafts, and therefore had temporarily put the planks across instead of erecting fences and filling them in. The Camborne magistrates imposed a fine of two guineas in respect of Woodward's shaft, one guinea in respect of another, and 5s. per day for 27 days from October 16, the period during which they had been left unfenced.[8] This case underlines the curious fact that West Wheal Lucy had literally been sunk in sand. Small wonder Eustice had been unable to persuade men to go down its shafts, which could so easily have collapsed and buried them.

1. MJ 1850 (16.11.)
2. MJ 1856 (16.2.)
3. *Cornish Telegraph* February 21 1872.
4. *Cornish Telegraph* August 28 1872.
5. *Cornish Telegraph* November 6 1872.
6. *Cornish Telegraph* December 16 1872.
7. *Cornish Telegraph* May 28 1873.
8. *Cornish Telegraph* June 18 1873.
9. *Cornish Telegraph* December 24 1873.
10. *Cornish Telegraph* January 19 1876.

WHEAL MARGARET

This mine is the most southerly of the Wheal Sisters group and exploited the same run of lodes as Wheal Kitty, which adjoins it on the E. The bal is an old one, its first recorded phase of working lasting from 1782 to 1804; a one-eighth share in the undertaking was advertised for sale in 1798.[1] Thomas Gundry, writing to Sir Christopher Hawkins on 21 April 1812 (in a letter preserved at the County Record Office, Truro) stated that "in the Manor of Trembethow, Wheal Marget *(sic)* has been given up some time, is worked deep and left off poor." The mine's greatest riches had, indeed, yet to be disclosed. It was restarted again in 1842, and by the middle of the century was making very handsome profits. At a typical quarterly account, held on February 22 1847, a dividend of £15 per 112nd share was paid (£1,680), the value of tin sold amounting to £4,468.[2]

But for this prosperity a grim price was exacted. A young miner called Thomas Uren, of Ludgvan died during July 1849 when a "scale" of ground fell on him from the back of a level.[3] A more serious accident occured around one p.m. on September 25 1851 when a "house of water" broke loose from an old shaft, abandoned 50 years before, into the 30 fm. level end, and in a short time filled 300 fms. of levels and 20 fms. depth of Engine shaft. It sent a blast of air before it which blew out most of the miners' candles, adding to the horror of their situation as they struggled to find their way out of the mine in total darkness. William Trebilcock, of Towednack, and William Johns, of Ludgvan, were boring a hole about 2 fms. up from the back of the 40 fm. level, and Trebilcock had just descended into the level when the water swept him forward 10 fms. towards the shaft where he was later found jammed between two wheelbarrows, quite dead. Johns, who remained in the back of the level, had a marvellous escape, as the water rose to his feet, and he remained in that dangerous situation for over an hour until rescued. Henry Reed and John Johns, of Ludgvan, were working in the bottom of a shaft 12 fms. below the 150 fm. level, when the water broke in. Both were drowned, their bodies being found by Capt. John Williams and others at midnight, after the flood had abated. They were in a very singular position, Reed being stretched out on the brace board of the shaft face downwards, whilst Johns appeared upright in the shaft, his head just in sight, apparently supported by a "dead hold-fast" which Reed had obtained with one hand on his clothing. Two other miners, Mathew Rodda, of Balnoon, and a lad called Samuel Kemp, of Polpeor, alarmed by the roaring of the water when working in the 160 fm. level, saved themselves by getting on the shaft platform whilst the flood descended around them, being assisted to safety after the cataract subsided. Several others had fortunate escapes, particularly the sumpmen, who, instead of being in their usual place at the shaft bottom, where they would have been drowned, were repairing timbers in the shaft of the 80 fm. level when the inundation occurred.[4]

There was good news for the adventurers at the December meeting in 1853. In addition to receiving a dividend of £13 per share, they learned that a splendid course of tin had been cut at the junction of the lodes in the 107 fm. level, worth at least £200 per fm.[5] At the March 1856 meeting, held at Halsetown, a dividend of £8 per 112th share, amounting to £896, was declared, the shares thereupon being divided into 448ths. The tin ground laid open was valued at £35-40,000.[6] A year later they cut a splendid course of tin in the 80 E. of Williams' shaft, on the Foul lode, worth from £30-40 per fm., with an end coming against it, 45 fms. off, worth £30 per fm.[7]

The affairs of Wheal Margaret at that time were directed by the celebrated Capt. Thomas Treweeke, of St. Ives, as purser; but at the September meeting a proposal to combine this appointment with that of principal agent was defeated at an election, 212 votes being recorded for Capt. Treweeke and 146 for Mr. William Darke, of Penzance.[8] It was said that the opposition to Capt. Treweeke was founded upon the principle that it was undesirable for any mine to be under the entire control of one family, however respectable; and it appeared from a circular issued by Mr. Bickford that Capt. Treweeke was already manager and his son clerk and carrier at Wheal Margaret.[9] The mine, however, was so well run and earning such splendid dividends that the majority of shareholders obviously thought it best to leave well alone.

The year 1859 proved an eventful one for the mine. She still continued to make excellent profits; but in July an alarming rumour began to circulate that Margaret's position as a prosperous dividend-payer was in serious jeopardy. For a long time it had been suspected that she was exceeding her boundaries. Two Botallack agents inspected the workings, and found that as much as £100,000 worth of tin had been taken from ground belonging to Wheal Mary, and that the South lode of the 40 ran into Wheal Kitty. As a consequence, Wheal Margaret's shares slumped in value, whilst Wheal Mary's increased, their respective quotations then being £60 and £440. The purser of Wheal Margaret came out with a public declaration that the alleged claims made by Mary against his mine were entirely without foundation. Later that month, his plans and diallings were examined by the adventurers, who expressed approval of the course he had pursued and confidence in the position of the mine.[10]

In May 1860 the "Old Blowing House Stamps," in Ludgvan, occupied by Wheal Margaret adventurers, as tenants to Edwin Ley, with the associated land, burning house, machinery, dressing floors, buddles and frames, were offered to let for a term of seven years, from midsummer. This was probably one of the sets of water stamps located in the valley below the mine.[11]

Margaret continued to achieve good profits for a few more years, but by 1863 she was making losses. In 1865 Thomas Spargo gave the depth of the mine as 25 fms. above adit and 180 fms. below. A hundred men, thirty women and forty boys were employed. The machinery included a 36″ pumping and stamping engine, a 24″ pumping engine, and two 24″ winding engines.

Two miners were seriously injured by a blasting accident in July 1866. One man, Williams, had part of his left hand blown off and was blinded, whilst the other, Maddern, had his upper and lower jaw broken but did not completely lose his sight. The powder was ignited by a spark from the tamping rod as they were driving the charge in a prepared hole.[12]

A report issued in November that year stated that Wheal Margaret, once so celebrated as a regular dividend paying concern, whilst still yielding fair returns, had scarcely a man working below the 60 fms. level, although the water was drained to below the 130 fm. level, at which point a very productive lode had been worked up to the boundary of Wheal Mary. Attempts had often been made to continue the working of this rich lode by arrangements between Wheal Mary and Wheal Margaret adventurers, but without success. "Provided such an agreement is not entered into, the whole of this valuable ground must remain, probably for many years, abandoned. One could hardly suppose that any such absurd policy will be adhered to, but . . . hope that both companies would, at such a depressed era in mining, gladly approach each other in a friendly spirit."[13] A few weeks afterwards it was reported that there was still a good chance of Wheal Margaret making an arrangement with Wheal Mary adventurers.[14] Some understandng does seem to have been reached between them for working the disputed ground, for the lower levels of Margaret were soon after put to work again. This recurring problem with Wheal Mary was one of the factors which eventually led to the consolidation of all the mines in this area under one management.

Margaret's fortunes revived in 1869. In June they began to open out a piece of ground between the 100 and 70 fm. levels which had been abandoned when the price of tin became low, but which, with its rise to around £71 a ton, could again be worked at a good profit. The mine re-entered the dividend list in September after a long absence, its shares having fallen to £3 in the interim, and the adventurers having met several calls. Altogether, £320,000 worth of tin had been raised, giving £68,000 in dividends and £14,000 in dues.[15]

In May 1872 the agents reported that the ground in the cross-cut, S. of Bramble shaft, had changed from a violently hard rock to a comparatively soft stone, indicative of the near proximity of the lode. The latter was in whole ground for the length of the sett; should it prove rich, the value of the property would be increased beyond that at any former period. A correspondent wrote that "this splendid old mine is like the Phoenix rising from its funeral pile . . . No mine in the district can compare favourably with this economical and well managed property." They were dressing a large quantity of tinstuff which had accumulated at surface in consequence of the great overflow of water during the previous winter. (One assumes that the dressing floors had been inundated, causing a suspension of operations.) They had enough material on hand to keep the stamps going for the greater part of a year.[16] Margaret made a handsome profit that quarter; but by August 1873 the book showed a debit of £1,292, equal to a call of 10s. per share. By October the shares were quoted at from 1-1½, or barely £1,000 for the mine. Faced with this worrying situation, the adventurers requested the lords to relinquish dues, and also sought permission to suspend the lower levels. An agent of one of the lords — Mr. Glanville — suggested that an amalgamation of Wheal Margaret and Wheal Kitty would be advantageous to both mines; and a committee was thereupon appointed to consult with Kitty on this matter, its members being T.S. Bolitho, H.P. Vivian, R.H. Bamfield and George Treweeke.[17] This may be regarded as the beginning of the concept of uniting all the mines of this group into a single large enterprise. The idea was given a further sharp impetus by an accident which occurred in Wheal Margaret in December 1874. An unsound adit collapsed through the decay of its timbers; and though for several days afterwards the men continued working as usual, rising water soon drove those in the lowest level from their pitches. Margaret was connected underground with both Kitty and Mary, and these also became affected. Between them, the three mines employed a total of 500 men, women and children, so that the prosperity of the entire district was threatened. Within three days the water had reached a depth of 50 fms. in Margaret. At Mary, the deepest of the three, 40 men were unable to work, with 20 or 30 more from the other mines. Efforts were meanwhile made to clear out the water by sinking shafts over the chokage. These eventually proved successful, and in less than a week the water level in all the mines was falling again.[18] Unhappily, the flooding soon after recurred, this situation leading to a decision being taken to combine all three into a single mine, called Wheal Sisters *(q.v.)*.

Margaret's returns prior to 1856 were large, but exact records have not survived. Between 1856-75 3,340 tons of black tin were sold for about £150,000.

1. *Sherborne Mercury* February 19 1798
2. *Penzance Gazette* February 24 1847
3. *West Briton* July 6 1849
4. *Royal Cornwall Gazette* September 1851
5. *Cornish Telegraph* January 18 1854
6. *Cornish Telegraph* March 5 1856
7. *Cornish Telegraph* March 25 1857
8. *Cornish Telegraph* September 2 1857
9. *Cornish Telegraph* August 19 1857
10. *Cornish Telegraph* July 9 1859; *West Briton* July 13 1859
11. *Cornish Telegraph* May 16 1860
12. *Cornish Telegraph* August 1 1866
13. *Cornish Telegraph* November 28 1866
14. *Cornish Telegraph* December 12 1866
15. *Cornish Telegraph* September 8 and October 20 1869
16. *Cornish Telegraph* May 1 and June 5 1872
17. *Cornish Telegraph* August 20, and October 1 and 22 1873
18. *Cornish Telegraph* December 1874

EAST WHEAL MARGARET (WHEAL MERTH, EAST WHEAL MERTH, WEST POLDICE, WHEAL ALICE)

In the steep sided valley running westwards from Canon's Town on the A30 Hayle—Penzance main road was located a group of ancient mines which exploited a series of E.N.E. trending lodes in metamorphosed killas and greenstone. Collurian Mine and South Wheal Kitty lay on the southern side of the valley, whilst on the opposite bank were Wheal Merth (near the stream), with East Wheal Margaret (also known as West Poldice, East Wheal Merth and Wheal Alice) about mid-way between Wheal Merth and Carntiscoe Farm. Downstream of Wheal Merth were Trevethoe Mine and Wheal Strawberry.[1]

The setts described here are those of Wheal Merth and East Wheal Margaret. The name Wheal Merth dates back to the 18th century, but the longest production run took place about a hundred years later under the name of East Wheal Margaret, in hopeful allusion to the highly successful Wheal Margaret, of the Wheal Sisters group, further to the west.

Between 1833-4 (as West Poldice) 220 tons of copper ore were raised, which fetched £1,618.[2] In 1839 a "peremptory sale" of materials by W. Tippet, auctioneer, took place at "West Poldice Mine, in the parish of Lelant." These comprised a steam engine, 56″ cylinder, with 36 heads of stamps; various pumps; two horse whims with shaft tackle, kibbles and chain; capstan and shears; 120 fms. of 12″ rope; large beam and scales; brass and iron weights; smiths' tools, bellows, anvils and vices; timbers; and buddles and frames.[3]

The mine reopened as East Wheal Margaret in 1849, continuing with varying success till 1865. In February 1853 the quarterly returns were given as 5 tons 17 cwt. 2 qrs. 27 lbs. of black tin, sold for £65 10s. per ton, amounting to £386 19s. 9d. The mine's appearance was improving, the 31 fm. level W. of "Curgonvin's" shaft being worth £35 per fm.[4] The March account for 1857 showed a three months' profit of £629 2s. 10d., but in June 1859 a rather sorry state of affairs was disclosed, the loss

MATERIALS FOR SALE BY PRIVATE CONTRACT,

AT EAST MARGARET MINE, LELANT, near the St. Ives Road Station, or about one mile from Hayle.

A 37-inch Cylinder Pumping Engine.
A 30-inch Cylinder Stamping Engine, 8 feet stroke, with 32 heads complete, a first class machine with 9 tons boiler.
A 20-inch cylinder winding engine, 4½ feet stroke, first class machine, with 9 ton boiler, cage and fly wheel, complete.
1 8 arm capstan complete.
150 fathoms, 8 to 12 inch pitwork, with matching pieces, H pieces, clack seat pieces, poles, stuffing boxes, glands, &c. complete, all in good condition.
60 fms. 2½ inch, 30 fms. 1¼ inch, and 20 fms. 1⅜ inch; iron pump rods.
3 horse whim complete.
200 fms. ⅝th inch horse whim chain.
Shaft tackle with 12 feet shieve.
2 new 12 feet shieves.
25 fms. new tram roads.
Wood and iron tram waggons.
Large quantity of flange and other bolts, of various sizes and lengths.
2 to 3 ton faggotted strapping plates.
4 to 5 ton scrap and old iron.
Several lots of new iron and steel. Stamps floors.
32 hand and patent frames, with launders and valves, complete.
20, 26 to 45 inch tin kieves.
Trunks, buddles, sheds, and dressing tools, complete.

SMITH'S SHOP.

2 36-inch bellows.
Anvils, vice, screwing stocks.
Mandrill, smiths' and miners' tools, complete.

ACCOUNT HOUSE FURNITURE,

Comprising tables, chairs,
Cooking apparatus, utensils,
Knives, forks, dinner set,
Tea set, &c., &c.

For further information apply to the agents on the mine, or to

MESSRS. HIGGS AND SON,
August, 1865. Albert Stores, Penzance.

being £620 and total debit balance £1,278, to reduce which a call of £1 was imposed. A letter from the lords' agents requesting the adventurers to resume some parts of the mine said to have been improperly worked having been read, it was resolved that the manager and purser should meet the agents "with a view to remove any erroneous conclusion they may have arrived at with reference thereto."[5]

Writing around 1864, Thomas Spargo noted that there had been a loss on the adventure, "and the prospects are not good enough to warrant a belief in its reimbursement." He had no fault to find with the management, however. The mine then employed 75 men, 16 women and 21 boys.

At the May meeting in 1865 it was reported that 19½ tons of tin had been sold for £959 8s. 6d., but a loss of £699 had been sustained on the quarter's working, and the shareholders accordingly resolved to offer the setts and materials for sale. The latter included a 37″ cylinder pumping engine; a 30″ cylinder stamping engine, 8′ stroke, with 32 heads, complete, "a first class machine with 9 tons boiler"; a 20″ cylinder winding engine, 4½′ stroke, with 9 tons boiler, cage and fly wheel, complete; a three-horse whim; pitwork; and account house furniture. It was said that £23,050 had been expended by the company in developing and working the mine.[6] Spargo's forebodings had thus, sadly, proved to be justified. It is curious to note that the auctioneer's sale announcement described the mine as being "near St. Ives Road Station" — *i.e.,* St. Erth — "or about one mile from Hayle" — doubtless a Cornish mile!

The mine appears to have been revived during the 1870's under another of its many aliases — Wheal Alice.[7] This appears to have been a fairly small scale operation, and the materials were offered for sale, without reserve, in 1877. The items included three stands for flat rods, with brackets and shieves; 55 fms. of 2¼″ round iron flat rods — of Irish design? — in eleven pieces; pumps; an overshot water wheel with 24″ launder; three stamp heads with iron lifters, and three others with wood lifters; two round buddles; and a small water wheel.[8]

On January 16 1879 it was reported that Mr. James Roach, when engaged in removing clay "from an old mine, formerly Wheal Merth" found, on arriving at the site one morning that all the ground on which he, with other workmen and three horses and carts had been working the previous day, had caved in, and a yawning shaft, several fathoms deep, had opened up, the covering sollar having given way. It was considered that all of them had had a miraculous escape from death.[9]

Around 1902 the sett was taken up by Mr. W. Gerry, who discovered some profitable tin ground. In 1903 he transferred the mine to a London syndicate, who developed it under its old name of Wheal Merth. By November most of the plant had been installed and the shaft was being vigorously sunk.[10] Soon afterwards the workings were partly flooded, but by early December the water had been pumped out, enabling the men who had been temporarily discharged to be taken on again.[11] Unfortunately, about two months later a lander was killed through his own forgetfulness in omitting to close the landing doors over the shaft when loading a waggon at surface; both he and the tram fell a distance of 72′.[12]

In October 1905 30 hands were employed on the mine.[13] In 1906 the Trevethoe Mining Co., who had been working it, transferred the property to Cornish Consolidated Tin Mines, Ltd. The Trevethoe Mining Co. had sunk a new shaft 30 fms. and then driven a cross-cut in the hope of striking a lode, but had not met with success, and the shaft had been abandoned, activity then being concentrated on one of the old shafts, 70 fms. deep. Here the Consolidated Co. erected one of Evans's steam pumps, fed by a marine boiler.[13] In June 1907 it was announced that after the water had been forked 30 fms. the piston valve of the pump broke, causing a temporary halt to the work. In this shaft men were stoping the backs at the 10 fm. level. It was intended to drain the shaft completely and then drive E. and W. Men were also stoping in an adit shaft E. of the central workings, 10 fms. in depth. Sixteen heads of stamps were being driven by a horizontal engine of 14½″ cylinder. These stamps had been idle three weeks, however, due to a breakage. Several E. — W. lodes ran through the sett, but the stuff recently produced had been of rather low grade, the average yield being just over 20 lb. to the ton.[14] These disappointing results seem to have led to the abandonment of the enterprise soon afterwards.

The two lodes in East Margaret were known as James's and Curgenvening's, the former being nearly vertical. The shafts were Engine, James's, New, Pool's, Davey's and Curgenvening's. Collins states that from 1833-4, 220 tons of copper ore were sold for £1,618, and from 1852-64 775 tons of black tin for about £54,000.

1. Dines, p. 136
2. Collins
3. *Royal Cornwall Gazette* December 6 1839
4. *Royal Cornwall Gazette* March 2 1853
5. *Cornish Telegraph* March 25 1857
6. *Cornish Telegraph* May 24 and 31 and September 6 1865
7. *Mining Journal* March 22 1873
8. *Cornish Telegraph* September 11 1877
9. *Cornishman* January 16 1879
10. *St. Ives Weekly Summary* November 7 1903
11. *St. Ives Weekly Summary* December 2 1903
12. *St. Ives Weekly Summary* January 30 1904
13. *St. Ives Weekly Summary* October 28 1905
14. *Western Echo* June 8 1907

LUDGVAN WHEAL MARGARET (COLLURIAN)

Situated on the southern side of the Canon's Town Valley about 350 yards S.E. of Carntiscoe farm, Ludgvan Wheal Margaret was reopened in 1849, and by 1864 had attained a depth of 87 fms., with no adit. It had 37″ pumping, 30″ stamping and 20″ winding engines; 112 people were employed. During 1864 64 tons of black tin were sold for £3,727 (Collins.) This sett appears to be identical, or nearly so, with Collurian Mine; and Dines (p. 137) gives an interesting account of exploration work carried out there on several occasions during this century, but the results were disappointing.

SOUTH WHEAL MARGARET

This sett was at Tregender Farm, Ludgvan, and during the early 19th century worked under the name of Tregender Mine. As South Wheal Margaret it was put on again in 1854, a call of £10 per share being made on January 22 to meet the initial outlay.[1] Little success attended the venture, however, and the sale of its machinery and materials was advertised to take place on December 9 1856. Among the items offered were a 26″ engine, quite new, 9′ stroke in cylinder and 8′ in shaft, for pumping and stamping, complete with boiler; two "stone whims" with shaft tackles (presumably these were for *hoisting* stone); and 70 fms. of iron stave ladders.[2] After a suspension of some years the mine was again put to work by a new group of adventurers. In January 1873 the prospects of South Margaret were said to be very encouraging. A considerable quantity of tinstuff was accumulating at surface, making the erection of a stamps advisable.[3]

1. *Royal Cornwall Gazette* February 10 1854
2. *Royal Cornwall Gazette* November 28 1856
3. *Cornish Telegraph* January 8 1873

WEST MARGARET

This mine, situated in Lelant, worked the same lodes as those in Wheal Margaret. According to J.H. Collins (1912) it sold between 1860-70 15 tons of black tin, valued at £1,082. The *Cornwall and Devon Mining Directory* of 1861 states that the company working it was in 3,000 shares, and had offices at St. Helen's Place, Bishopsgate; the secretary was G. Lavington (London), purser, James Hollow, manager Thomas Uren (of East Providence), and agent, W. White. The 1870 edition of the same publication gives the engineers as Francis Michell and William Jenkin; the mine was then 75 fms. deep and employed 20 persons.

WHEAL MARY

This is one of the Wheal Sisters group, its near "relatives" Margaret and Kitty bordering it respectively on the S. and E., with Wheal Reeth lying to the N. on the slope of Trink Hill. Wheal Mary is the northernmost of the six lodes which course in a generally E.N.E. direction through the combined Wheal Sisters setts, and was opened on at New Engine, Hyde's, Horton's, Old Engine, Oxley's and Wheal Mary shafts. Another lode lies to the N.E. of Wheal Mary lode, the shafts here being Field's, and Michell's. The mine is undoubtedly ancient; but the earliest phase of working known from actual records dates only from the 1820's. When 4-50th shares were offered for sale in February 1826 it was stated that she had recently commenced working, "and is a promising Adventure, being only 35 fms. deep; adjoining Wheal Reeth and Wheal Margaret Mines, both of which have been very productive, and Wheal Reeth is at present the best Tin Mine in this County."[1] In 1838 163 people were employed, the workings being drained by a 20″ engine.

Wheal Mary fully justified the faith of her backers, and proved very rich for tin. She also increased considerably in depth, as shown by the details of an accident which occurred there in 1849. As a young man named Richard Stevens, of Try, in Gulval, was wheeling tin stuff to a platform in the 90 fm. level, his candle, as it was supposed, went out, and in going for a light he missed the ladder road, walked to the shaft and fell 50 fms. to his death.[2] This gives a minimum depth of 140 fms. for the shaft.

In February 1859, when a dividend of £1,000 (£10 per 100th share) was distributed, the adventurers decided to subdivide the mine into 500 shares. Between 1860-62 a short-lived working arrangement was entered into with Wheal Kitty under the name of Mary and Kitty United, foreshadowing the later, more comprehensive combination known as Wheal Sisters.

Capt. Matthew Curnow, underground agent at Wheal Mary, gave some interesting particulars relating to the mine when he appeared before Lord Kinnaird's Royal Commission on August 2 1862. About 110 men were employed underground. The lowest level was the 160 below adit; it was quite a cold level — "there is a breeze of wind there, and the men are glad to stand in it sometimes." They generally worked in pairs of two men each for a period of six or seven hours, three pairs being employed in the twenty-four hours. He thought that the practice of working single-handed, as at St. Just, was harder for the borers — "a man must use more strength to beat the work by himself as compared with two men." The mine charged the men 9d. a lb. for candles, their cost price being about 6s. or 6s. 6d. per dozen lbs. Their gunpowder was the ordinary common powder, made in the county; for this, the miners paid 8d. per lb. Deductions were made of 6d. each for the club and doctor. The club money was paid to men injured by accidents; it was not for sickness; but if a man were laid up for a long time, they considered it a kind of charity to support him from these funds rather than that he should apply for relief elsewhere. There were two doctors, chosen by a canvas. "I have attended meetings where, in putting on mines, we have taken up shares to carry on a mine, and that has been canvassed before the adventurers and carried there, and then the labouring men must take whoever is fixed on to attend them; but ours was carried by a majority of the men." Under questioning, he conceded that the mine made a profit both by the sale of candles and powder, but maintained that the price of these articles was kept high to induce the men not to be extravagant in their use, and so get involved in too much expense — "it is different to pay for a thing at a dear price to what it is in coming and taking it away at a cheap price; if I take up a thing that I pay for heavily I must take care of it." A stream of pure water was conveyed underground for the men to drink — "it is good for their health when eating their morsel." Curnow stated he had worked underground as a miner for over thirty years, twenty-eight of these in Wheal Mary, the last seventeen as agent; he was then in his fiftieth year, but had never suffered in health from being a miner.

Spargo, in 1865, gave the depth of adit as 22 fms., and depth under adit 170 fms. The labour force comprised 118 men, 23 females and 14 boys. There were two pumping engines (22″ and 24″) and two winding engines (18″ and 20″), whilst three stamping mills were worked by water wheels. A few years afterwards the latter were replaced by a 40″ steam engine with new stamps. In 1869 it was said that the mine had raised £325,000 worth of tin and made a profit of £42,000.[3] A new engine house and smiths' shop were reported to be under construction in October 1872. A year later Wheal Mary was described as a "quiet"-unpublicised-mine, almost unknown outside her own district. "(She) is in the hands of a few, local, unobtrusive shareholders, who stick to her, and know nothing of transfers or brokers. The mine has made £10,000 profit within a very few years. Her proprietors also own an adjacent mine — Trencrom — and a good deal of Wheal Mary's profit has been devoted to the succour of her less successful sister."[4] A fine rock of tin was sent to surface at about this time from a place which resembled a railway cutting, where the lode was fully exposed to view.

A singular accident occurred in June 1873. William Johns, William Stevens and other tutworkers were sinking a winze from the 160 to the 170 fm. level, and had bored a hole from the bottom of the partly sunk winze with the intention of putting it through to the 170. The 8′ drill not being long enough to go completely through the remaining 9′ of intervening ground, they decided to pack 4 lbs. of powder — "an unusual charge for an unusual purpose" — into the hole, and try to blast through to the lower level. Johns charged the hole, and Stevens lit the fuse, both then ascending to the 160 to be out of the way. After the blast they went back to the winze, expecting to find the powder had broken through.

Stevens volunteered to be lowered into the winze and inform his comrades if the communication had been made. Against Johns' better judgement, he was let down, but on reaching the bottom reported that the smoke was hot, and asked to be drawn up. Johns raised him about 3 or 4 fms., but then Stevens fell away, and made no response to the shouted enquiries of his comrades. John Allen then put a strap round his shoulders and was lowered to the bottom where he found Stevens lying dead. Allen himself then became unconscious, but after about twenty minutes partially recovered, got into the rope and was wound up. At the inquest on Stevens, held at the "Lamb and Flag,"St. Erth, the jury returned a verdict of "accidental death," but could not decide whether this had resulted from a blow received when he fell out of the "slug," or suffocation caused by inhaling gunpowder smoke.[6]

The later history of this mine is given under Wheal Sisters, which Wheal Mary joined on its formation in 1875.

It may, however, be appropriate to relate here a little known fact connected with the mine. Adjacent to the road at Brunnion Farm is a shaft on which some years ago stood a wind pumping engine to supply water to the farm; it is believed that the old name of this shaft was Wheal Pink. The story goes that, during the Napoleonic period some French prisoners of war were put to work in the Brunnion shaft; and that whilst engaged underground they sculptured with their crude miners' tools a two feet high carving of the Virgin Mary on the sidewall of the level. The carving still exists, but can only be seen during dry weather when the water level has fallen sufficiently to enable the place to be visited. It is possible that the name "Wheal Mary" derives from this sculpture.[5] In this connection it is interesting to note that the historian Davies Gilbert mentions that at "Amelibrea" were (in 1838) "the remains of an extensive foundation said by tradition to have formerly supported a prison." It seems possible that this prison at Amalebra, in Towednack, may have housed the French prisoners who made this carving.

Collins gives the following statistics for the mine: from 1837-9 and 1848-76, 3,940 tons of black tin; 1860-2 (Mary and Kitty United) 80 tons of black tin.

1. *Royal Cornwall Gazette* February 18 1826
2. *Royal Cornwall Gazette* July 13 1849
3. *Cornish Telegraph* October 20 1869
4. *Cornish Telegraph* November 1 1873
5. *Cornish Telegraph* June 25 1873
6. Per Mr. Henry Symons, St. Ives, who has personally seen the sculpture.

WHEAL MARY AND ROSE

Among the effects of John Stevens, a bankrupt, advertised to be peremptorily sold by auction at the house of David Kiskeys, innkeeper, at "Crowlass," in Ludgvan, on January 31 1815, were 25-64th parts in a tin mine called Wheal Mary and Rose, in the tenement of "Vorvas" (Worvas), Lelant. The sett comprised many valuable lodes and was very extensive; it also had the advantage of Wheal Crack deep adit, enabling it to be worked at small expense.[1] Wheal Crack was one of the Wheal Speed group of mines, some shares in which were also offered at this time.

1. *Royal Cornwall Gazette* January 21 1815

MOUNT TIACK

The Mount Tiack Tin and Copper Mining Company, with offices in Throgmorton Street, London E.C., possessed a capital (in May 1852) of 4,500 £1 shares. The mine worked by this cost-book concern measured a mile from east to west and three-quarters of a mile from north to south. It included the setts of Mount Tiack, Barsheba (Beersheba), Lapurian, part of Trurom (Trencrom) and the adjoining commons, and contained six lodes which had been worked by old men, the three most northern being Mount (on which a shaft was sunk), Trevaskis and Pump. The

St. Ives Tin Stamp, Lamb & Flag. (M.)

mine was held from W. B. Praed for 21 years at 1/18th dues.

Operations were in progress in the spring of 1852, when the manager (Capt. Hosking) reported that the mine, which was being unwatered, was "looking excellent," and stamps were constantly at work. An engine bought by the company would enable the shaft to be sunk a further 40 fathoms, and two great champion lodes, one three feet wide and the other four feet, were expected to meet at a point ten fathoms below the shaft bottom. There was also "a gulph of tin" in the bottom. The shaft was on Mount lode.

By June 1852 £60 worth of tin ore had been raised during the opening, for two fathoms, of one of the south lodes. Information concerning the mine was offered by Weatherly, the secretary and purser, who published favourable reports on it. The shares were offered for sale in October 1852, when it was stated that since work had been started two of the south lodes had been found to be rich at a shallow depth. Ore was being raised and dressed and it was proposed to erect 24 heads of stamps. A favourable report had been made on the mine by Capt. John Roberts of Halamanning and Croft Gothal. The shares were listed among those of the producing mines in the *Mining Journal* from May 1852 to August 1856.[1]

1. *Mining Journal* May 1 1852, June 5 1852, June 12 1852, October 16 1852; 1852-6 lists. See also Dines (1956) p. 135 (Trevarrack; New Trencrom.) (Per Justin Brooke.)

WHEAL NANTZ

A correspondent wrote in the *Mining Journal* of October 27 1849 that operations at Wheal Nantz, Lelant, were progressing highly satisfactorily. The sett, which immediately adjoined Wheal Reeth, contained the same lodes. It was contemplated to extend the sphere of operations, and returns were expected almost to equal the monthly cost. This mine may subsequently have been worked as Nance Valley, though this title may have been applied to a mine in Illogan parish.

WHEAL NINNES

In the valley to the south of Trencrom Hill lies the little hamlet of Ninnesbridge, which probably owes its origin to an old tin mine called Wheal Ninnes, 6-64th shares in which were offered for sale in 1823 at £5 per share.[1] In April 1830 John Davey, of Marazion, aged 30, whilst removing a "plump" (? pump) from the Engine shaft at this mine received fatal injuries when the bar slipped, precipitating him thirteen fathoms.[2] During the following year, a case came on at the Cornwall Assizes in which Harvey & Co., general merchants of Hayle, successfully sued James Andrews and his co-adventurers in "Wheal Ninnes Mine, in the parish of Lelant," for £161, being the value of timber, iron and coal supplied to them.[3] It is interesting to note that the deeds of Ninnesbridge Chapel, built in 1872, describe that property as being "bounded . . . on the East by the Stream coming out of Ninnis Audit."[4] The spelling of "audit" here accurately preserves the old pronounciation of this word.

1. *Royal Cornwall Gazette* November 8 1823
2. *Royal Cornwall Gazette* May 1 1830
3. *Royal Cornwall Gazette* April 9 1831
4. Noall, Cyril, *History of the St. Ives Fore Street Methodist Church,* 1962

WHEAL NORTH

The notorious E. Harvey Archer Wadge of Plympton wrote in September 1904 referring to a celebrated mining manager who had said some years before that nothing worthwhile was to be found over six miles west of Camborne and thirty miles East of it. He advised him "not to ventilate his opinion on the subject in the presence of those interested in the masterly exploiting of Wheal North in Lelant . . . with splendid results." (This was not a misprint for Wheal Merth.)

Alfred E. Doidge, M.E., of Perranwell, wrote a month later that Wheal North had been opened in recent years and was now working in virgin ground on an old mine, which he listed with "a few of the most important" of recent mining developments.[1]

1. MW 1904 (17.9, 15.10.)

WHEAL PENCROM

This mine, situated in Lelant parish, was said in 1870 to be 15 fms. deep and employing six people.

PORTHREPTA BEACH WORK

An old Carbis Bay resident (Mr. William Payne) has recorded that a six-head stamps, with the usual dressing plant, formerly stood on the site of the Orange Tea Rooms (now a car park) on Porthrepta Beach. The stamps were fed (with water) from Wheal Providence, and stamped deposits known as "beach work." The latter's availability was dependant on a north wind, and when things were set for a good "coat," just a slight variation of the wind would cause the sea to re-mix the tin with the sand, making the operation useless.

Hunt's *Mineral Statistics* states that sales from the "beach at Carbis Water" in 1859 amounted to £98 18s. 10d. In 1860 the output of 1 ton 9 c. 0 q. 7 lbs. of black tin realised £156 13s. 8d. In 1880 1 ton 1 c. 0 q. 18 lbs. realised £46 13s. 10d. An almost identical amount sold in 1881 for £66 2s. 6d. The occupier in 1887 was Edward Payne, who employed five workers.

PRAED CONSOLS

The sett of Praed Consols embraces the southern and south western flanks of Trencrom Hill; included with it is Wheal Cherry, *q.v.* The workings lay to the north of the hamlet of Ninnesbridge, being centred on Tyringham shaft. The early history of this mine is very obscure. The *Cornwall and Devon Mining Directory* of 1861 gives the name of its purser as W. Darke and the manager J. Stevens. Spargo, in 1865, identifies it with Wheal Cherry, adding that, after the erection of machinery, it soon went down for want of capital. In 1870 a sett described as "Old Wheal Praed, Lelant," was reported to have been taken up and set to work by Capt. Tom Richards.[1]

In the early part of this century the sett appears to have been extended, to take in Mount Lane mine, and was given the name of New Trencrom, or Trencrom Hill mine. The lodes, trending roughly E.N.E., are known as Wheal Cherry, North, and South, and the shafts as China Clay, Engine, Wheal Cherry and East, all being comparatively shallow. At various times between 1907 and 1943 a little prospecting seems to have been carried out, but production of black tin was minimal. See Dines, p. 135.

1. *Cornish Telegraph* April 6 1870

WHEAL PROVIDENCE (PROVIDENCE MINES)

From the north western half of Porthrepta (Carbis Bay) beach a rich belt of mineralised ground extends inland to the eastern flank of Worvas Hill. Here formerly stood the tall engine houses and other buildings of one of the great mines of this district — Wheal Providence — which gave employment to hundreds of men, women and children and a never-failing succession of dividends to the fortunate adventurers. It takes a real effort of imagination to visualise this scene of busy activity today, for the sprawling surface remains of this large enterprise have been almost totally obliterated, the engine houses at Wheal Speed and on the cliff cast down, the huge red burrow above Carbis Water levelled, and the dressing floors buried beneath the concrete and tarmac of ever spreading housing estates. Should the ghosts of the "old men" ever revisit the scene of their former labours they would find scarce one familiar feature remaining, save, perhaps, the fine old count house at Chyangweal and the copper stained adits on the beach.

The mine took its name from one of a number of small undertakings which were active here during the 18th and early 19th centuries. In 1780 the Rev. John Swete, when making a tour of Cornwall, visited one of these mines — he does not specify which — and wrote an interesting description of what he saw. His account was published a few years ago in the Journal of the Royal Institution of Cornwall, and only its more salient points need be mentioned here. Swete, with a friend and a servant, descended the five feet diameter shaft, from whose ladder several staves were missing, holding lighted farthing candles. At a depth of about thirty fathoms they began to crawl through a lengthy adit, where they received a drenching from a vessel of water drawn up to and emptied in their level by workmen at surface who were ignorant of their presence in the mine. Continuing their explorations, they were obliged to pass over "a deep, dark gulph" by crawling along a plank on hands and knees, and then make their way by steep and rugged ascents and declivities until they had reached a depth of about eighty fathoms. Here the lode, a tolerably rich one, was encountered, and Swete obtained a specimen from it, said to be "all tin, saving a very little spar." Returning to surface, he inspected the horse whim by which both ore and water were drawn from the mine in kibbles. Descending the hill on their return to St. Ives they saw tin stuff being broken down by a water stamps, the axle of the wheel having three wooden teeth which alternately lifted up three perpendicular logs, these crushing the material in their fall. This was then passed through a grate and washed in "buddels" to produce the refined black tin.

During the following 30 years considerable progress was made in extending and equipping these mines. In March 1810, when a few of its 64th shares were offered for sale, Wheal Providence was described as "that very promising Copper Mine . . . in Lelant, Cornwall, now in full course of working; has a good Steam-Engine, and is throwing up a great quantity of Ore of superior quality."[1] Despite this, its materials were put

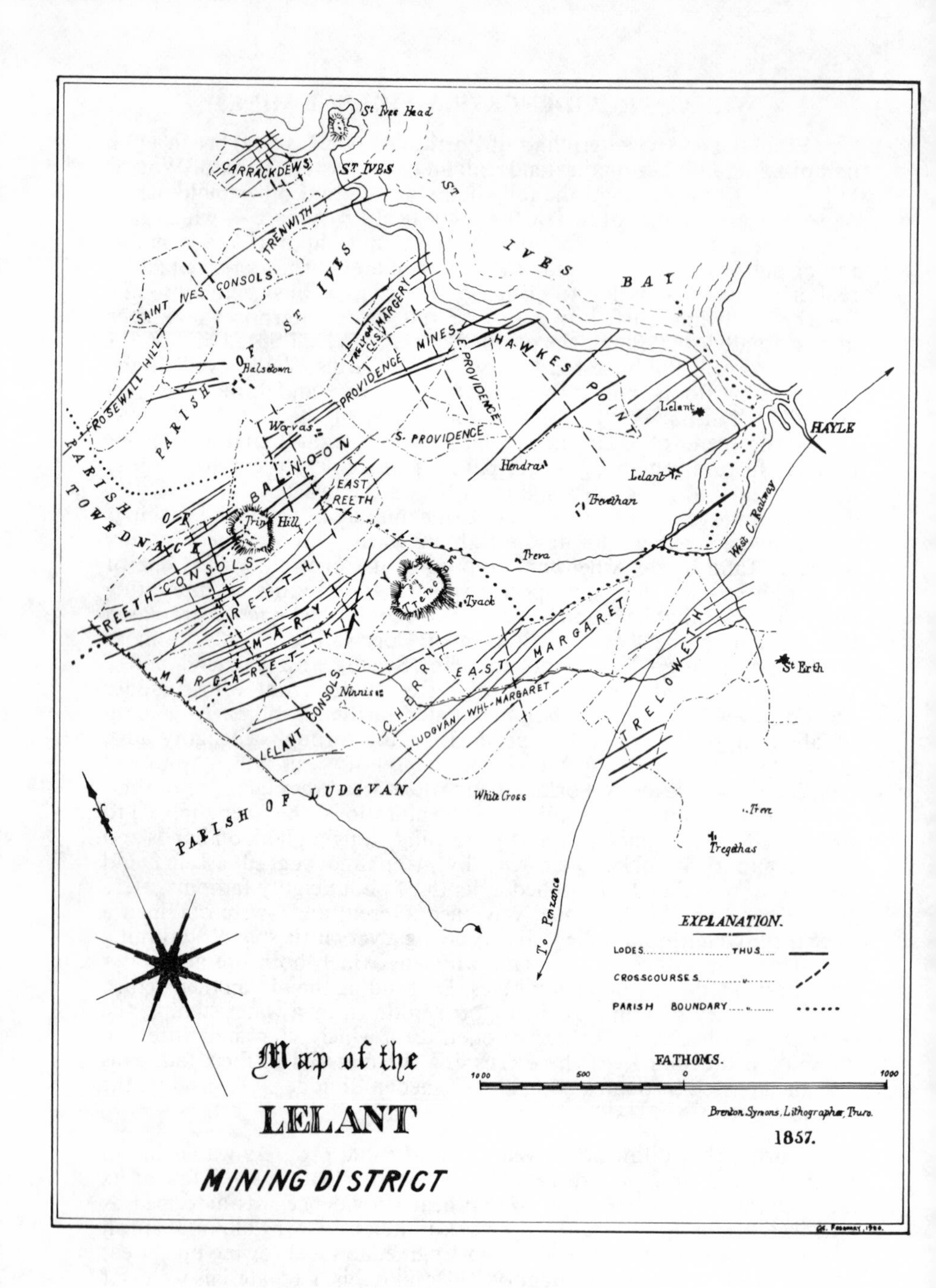
St Ives Head
CARRACKDEWS
ST IVES
TRENWITH
SAINT IVES CONSOLS
ST IVES BAY
ROSEWALL HILL
PARISH OF ST IVES
Halsetown
PROVIDENCE MINES
E. PROVIDENCE
HAWKES POINT
Lelant
HAYLE
S. PROVIDENCE
Worvas
BALNOON
EAST REETH
Hendra
Lelant
Trevethan
PARISH OF TOWEDNACK
Trink Hill
Trera
REETH CONSOLS
REETH
Trencrom
Tyack
MARY KITTY
MARGARET
EAST MARGARET
TRELOWETH
West C. Railway
St Erth
Ninnis
CHERRY
LUDGVAN WHL MARGARET
LELANT CONSOLS
PARISH OF LUDGVAN
White Cross
Tregethas
To Penzance
EXPLANATION.
LODES............THUS
CROSSCOURSES.........
PARISH BOUNDARY.........
FATHOMS.
1000
500
0
1000
Map of the
LELANT
MINING DISTRICT
Brenton Symons, Lithographer, Truro.
1857.

up for auction a few months later. These included a good 20″ cylinder engine, double power, "on Messrs. Bolton and Watt's plan of erection;" a water pressure engine "with a Brass Cylinder, for little Pistons to work in;" pumps; capstan and capstan rope; shears; shieves; and three good whims, with ropes and kibbles. All these items were said to be nearly new.[2]

Wheal Providence lay on the cliffs just N. of Carbis Valley; and Joseph Carne, writing in 1821, stated that its 24 and 32 fm. levels had been driven 20 fms. under the sea. Dr. Hamilton Jenkin has recorded a tradition that as late as the mid-19th century mules were employed to carry up ore from Engine Shaft, just below the present railway line.

It has been stated by several writers that the amalgamation of the various small mines hereabouts to form the so-called Providence Mines took place in 1832. This, however, requires some qualification, as an advertisement published in 1815 makes abundantly clear. The assignees of John Stevens, a bankrupt, therein offered for sale 2-45th parts in "the United Mines of Wheal Comfort, Wheal Speed, Wheal Hazard, and East and West Wheal Crack, with the materials, situate in Lelant: — each of these Mines formerly constituted a separate Adventure, but being now consolidated, the Set is very extensive, and many valuable Lodes run through them." The auction was to take place at the house of David Kiskeys, innkeeper, in "Crowlass," Ludgvan, on January 31.[3] The advantage of working these mines on a joint basis was thus realised and put into practice much earlier than has generally been supposed. Wheal Providence joined, and gave its name to the grouping in 1832; and it was this event which launched the undertaking on its great career; but the foundations for it were laid by the earlier consolidation.

Providence Mines, as constituted in 1832, included also the ancient bals of Wheal Laity and Good Fortune. It was divided at first into 112 shares, but as the workings improved in value these were increased to 560 and eventually to 1,120.

Several reports written by Joseph Vivian afford glimpses of the mines shortly after their consolidation. On November 15 1834 he described "Wheal Providence" as a copper mine which had been partially worked "about 30 years ago" by a small steam engine, but was abandoned for lack of sufficient engine power and capital. The workings had been carried about 40 fms. below adit, the adit level workings being extended to a much greater length than those below. Several thousand pounds' worth of copper had been produced, but the mine had not met cost. On March 20 1835 he noted that a steam engine had been purchased for "the Comfort, or as we now call it, the Providence Mines." Previous to this, Wheal Comfort, *q.v.*, had been reported on separately. On July 10 1836 Vivian stated that they had sampled 50 tons of copper worth about £15 a ton. The 12 fm. level continued very good, whilst the 22, 32, 42 fm. levels and Engine shaft sinking under the 42 were all producing a little ore. All these levels were driving W. — inland. Wheal Whidden lode had been intersected in the 22 cross-cut, rather poor, but would save tin. Laity adit continued poor, ground hard.

By 1838 considerable quantities of copper ore were being produced. The mine then had a 30″ engine and employed 132 people. Mr. Samuel Higgs, appointed as the Providence Mines' first purser, was for many years faced with a difficult uphill task to bring the enterprise to a state of profitability. In this, he was effectively supported by the lords — Praed of Trevetho, the Basset family, Stephens of Tregenna Castle, and Gilbert — who relinquished dues altogether from March 1840 to May 1849. They all had unlimited faith in the future of this great mine, and were willing to make every effort to bring it safely through the protracted development stage.

A few facts and figures will help to illustrate their dogged pertinacity and courage. The capital paid in by the original shareholders up to May 1848, when profits were first achieved, amounted to £10 6s.7d. per share, or £11,569 8s. 1d. During that time £53,940 was received for copper ore; £34,746 18s. 4d. for tin; £26 4s. 4d. for pitchblende; and £1,937 12s. 1d. for sundries. During this same period of sixteen years £102,220 2s. 10d. was expended on labour and materials, without any return by way of dividends to the adventurers or of dues to the lords. But their faith and patience were to be richly rewarded, as will be subsequently seen. This ultimate success would not have been achieved but for the high output — principally of copper — from the old Wheal Providence part of the sett, whose value up to May 1846 amounted to £51,715 15s. 5d. That section then failed, and was abandoned, but not before it had made a vital contribution to the success of the undertaking.

It was probably the reorganisation contingent on the closing of old Wheal Providence that led to the auctioning of a quantity of materials at the Providence Mines in February 1847. Among the items disposed of were an excellent 30″ cylinder pumping engine with 7 tons boiler — "for duty performed, see Lean's Reporter for 1844 and 5;" a very superior steam whim of 18″ cylinder; and a water pressure engine of 8″ cylinder "with nozzles on the most approved plan."[4] The sale proved only partially successful; and when the 30″ engine was re-offered for sale by private contract in March, intending purchasers were instructed to apply to Capt. Penberthy on the mines — presumably Sir Henry Irving's uncle, who lived at Halsetown.

The dividends paid in 1848 amounted to £2,590 or £2 6s. 3d. per share. From then, for a period of more than twenty years, large and regular annual profits were made. Payment of dues was resumed in May 1849, the lords thus reaping their share of the rich golden harvest which the mine provided. In the November account of 1856 over 58 tons of tin were reported sold during the quarter at an average price of more than £80 a ton, with ten tons still in stock; and the dividend paid amounted to £2,240, or £4 per 560th share, making a total of £10,080 divided that year.[5] In the context of such prosperity the destruction of the "dry" by fire, together with the underground clothes of more than a hundred men, in July, 1858, must have seemed a relatively trifling misfortune — except, of course, to the unfortunate miners themselves.[6]

During that year arrangements were concluded with the neighbouring Trelyon Consols mine for the joint working of Trelyon Downs bounds under the name of ''Providence and Trelyon United,'' both parties sharing expenses and profits. (See under Trelyon Consols.) 1859 witnessed the high water mark of the mine's good fortune. During that year a total of £10 7s. 9d. per share, amounting to £11,634, was distributed, a sum slightly exceeding the paid-up capital. Altogether, more than £50 per share had been paid since 1848, this representing about a third of the value of the produce during that period. At the November meeting it was decided to increase Capt. Arundel Anthony's salary to £14 14s. per month, on the understanding that he gave the whole of his time to managing the mines.[7] In 1860 profits were slightly lower, £8,680 or £7 15s. per share being distributed in dividends, whilst in 1861 these amounts were further reduced to £4,480 and £4, at around which level they remained for several years thereafter.

Providence Mines soon after closure, c. 1880. (M, E.A.)

The agents' report for April 1860 stated that in Higgs' shaft No. 3 carbona was worth £30 per fm. and No. 4 carbona £20. The winze from the 75 to the 85 was holed and they were stoping E. from it, lode worth £20 per fm. No. 1 stope in the bottom of the level was worth £80 per fm. Dunstan's shaft had been communicated with the 55 and a skip road was being prepared to draw from it. In Little Wheal Speed shaft the 35 fm. level was driving W. on the North lode, worth £5 per fm., and E. on the South lode, worth £6 per fm. In Trelyon Lower Mine the lode in the 16 fm. level driving E. was worth £12 per fm. They had begun to clear Hocking's shaft from surface; this had been sunk about 6 fms. below adit by the former workers, and would be sunk to the 16 fm. level with all despatch. A new railroad had been completed from Higgs' shaft to the new stamps spalling floors, to facilitate the discharge of tinstuff; a branch would be extended to Dunstan's shaft on a viaduct. 120 fms. of railroad had also been completed in the 65 level on the Standard and New South lodes. A trip plot and railroad were being installed in the 85 fm. level.

In February 1862 it was announced that the driving of the 65 E. from No. 2 carbona on an E. and W. lode at Higgs' shaft had been resumed. This carbona was ventilated from a cross-cut in the 75, which had opened an important part of the mine, the working of which had been suspended for several years. On New South lode, No. 1 stope below the 65 E. was worth £120 per fm., and other stopes £50 and £30. In the North ground a new perpendicular flat rod shaft was being sunk to meet the lode about 15 fms. from surface; they were also driving the deep adit N. to drain it and facilitate the opening of this part of the sett. In Trelyon Lower Mine the flat rod and lifts had been removed to Daniel's shaft, which was being cleared and secured below the deep adit with all possible speed. In July, a horse whim and skip road were being fixed on Flat Rod shaft, which would delay its sinking for about ten days.

In August 1862 the two principal officials of the mine — Capt. William Hollow, who had succeeded Capt. Arundel Anthony as manager, and the purser, Mr. Samuel Higgs — gave evidence to Lord Kinnaird's Commission appointed to enquire into the condition of mines. Hollow described Providence as principally a tin mine; the greatest depth from surface was 170 fms., the lowest working level being at 130 fms. They had no close ends, the greatest distance from shaft being about 110 fms. Several winzes were worked on tribute in the 130, the nearest about 10 fms. from the end. Asked whether they sank winzes only for ventilation, he replied: "Not in the Providence mines; our mines are very singular; we are not like many other mines on the course of the lode. The greater portion of our operations are off the lode. If the lode is E. or W., the greater part of our operations will be going N. and S., or N.E. and S.W., so that we can hardly give an estimate." In the eastern section, however, the lode was normal, and productive, and there winzes were sunk at regular intervals for ventilation only. In addition to these, they made use of a ventilating machine, called a piston, by which air was pumped from a cylinder through 5″ iron pipes by the engine to within two fathoms of the ends, just out of the way of the blasting. The engine worked at 8-10 strokes per minute. They had had this device for two years, but it was only used "on very particular occasions."

When blasting on the lode, smoke cleared from the ends in about half-an-hour, enabling work to be quickly resumed, but elsewhere they only blasted once a day, just before leaving work. They usually only worked a single core (spelt "corps" in the report). "We find that men will do better in a single corps than by working four in a pair." The men went down at six and came up at two. Only in a few instances were they replaced by a second core. Hollow explained that by a "single corps" he meant two men working 8 hours out of 24. Their reason for having only one core was that there were so many parts in the mine they wished to try; and they thought that by putting on up to 20 tutwork bargains, more discoveries would be made. Whenever this occurred, they put on from two to four; "the mine is so bunchy that we are constantly trying."

During the seven years Capt. Hollow had been working in Providence there had not been one blasting accident. The men were supplied with a hard piece of wood for settling the powder, but the tamping process was finished off with an iron rod. "Our ground is all dry ground, perhaps that may be in favour of our not having such accidents as there might be in wet ground." The men ascended and descended by ladders. These were mostly 20′ long, and occasionally 23′. Tools were sent up and down by the steam whim, the men not being allowed to carry them. Changing in the boiler houses was forbidden, there being a good dry on the mine. The women worked under cover, a separate house being provided for them. "We take all the care we can," added the witness cryptically.

Under further questioning, Capt. Hollow gave additional information regarding the ventilating engine. This was not at surface, but fixed down in the shaft at one of the airiest places available. The cylinder was 20″ diameter, with a 6′ stroke; it resembled the cylinder of a steam whim. It would pump air 150 fms., and blow out a candle at some distance from the mouth. The air supply could be divided, as the cylinder pumped two strokes of air to one stroke of the engine, and they might put one stroke E. and the other W., if that were needed, but usually only one end required ventilating.

They suffered from no scarcity of labour; "in fact, we are so swarmed with (men) that we hardly know what to do with them." The lode was priced at from £4 10s. to £6. Asked if he thought it was necessary to have two men to break ground at this price, he replied that the men in their district did not like working single-handed (as at St. Just) — in fact, they could not do it.

Mr. Samuel Higgs' evidence was of a more general kind, and related largely to the method of paying the men, the supply of candles and powder (the latter being described as "the rough kennel powder," that is, from the Kennal Vale powder works, near Penryn); and provisions for the men's welfare. At Providence, 4d. in the £ of the miners' earnings was deducted for the doctor and club. At the purser's discretion, payments could be made from the club in case of sickness, or injury. Surplus club money was divided among the adventurers, in accordance with that shameful old Cornish practice. Currently, they had a balance in hand for the club of £268 13s. 5d. About fourteen years ago the mine had been very poor, and the hands were much reduced; they then had £260 in the club, £100 of which were transferred to the adventurers. Asked why the men were obliged to contribute a percentage of their earnings to the club instead of a fixed sum per month, Higgs replied that he found the Providence mine very bunchy, and the tributers would go sometimes for up to six months and get scarcely anything, and then received a very small subsist; but yet their cost was always charged for the doctor and club, as a debt against the men. This was paid by the adventurers; but when the men got a "sturt" of £20 or £30 each they were only charged 1s. The tributers now earned an average of just over £3, and the 4d. came in regularly and was no loss to the adventurers. No payment was deducted for the barber; "that is rather a barbarous practice, and it is going out." The pun, one hopes, was unintentional.

In September 1863 Samuel Higgs, jun., became joint purser with his father; and at the same time Capt. Hollow's salary was increased by two guineas, and Capt. Rogers' and Dunstan's one guinea each per month.[8] In September 1865 the adventurers showed their appreciation of the long and faithful service given by Samuel Higgs, sen., by presenting him with a testimonial of plate, equal in value to 2s. 6d. per share (£150.) He had held the pursership for nearly 35 years and divided £86,520 profits. Because of the current mining depression, Providence was then the only dividend-paying mine in the St. Ives district, so that the shareholders had every reason to feel gratified. The occasion was a happy one, and inevitably the speakers tended to be in reminiscent mood. Mr. Higgs himself recalled how Providence Mines had been started with 12 adventurers and were first successful in copper, obtained from near and under the sea. What was thus gained, they spent again in opening those parts of the mine which now yielded tin. It was a long time before success came, and their agents, from one cause or another, were frequently changed. First came Capt. Henry Francis, followed by Capt. Vivian, who retired owing to pressure of other engagements. It was then decided to appoint agents who should give their entire attention to the mine; and under the agency of Capts. Rowe and Isaac Penberthy they paid their first dividends. Capt. Penberthy died. Then came Capt. Dunstan; and the permanency of the mine was largely owing to his skill in opening and working it. After his retirement through ill health Capt. Anthony took over, but left within a few years to seek his fortune abroad. He was succeeded by Capt. Hollow, their present agent. Since leaving the mine, Capt. Dunstan had died, his death in some degree accelerated by the exertions he had made in extinguishing a fire in one of the engine houses; steps would be taken for the relief of his widow and three children.

Referring to the sickness club, Mr. Higgs said they charged 4d. in the £ for the club and doctor, and had found that amount quite sufficient for all visible hurts and sickness. "If a man happens to die and leaves a family, we have a rule that meets such a sad case of sickness and destitution; that rule briefly is — that a miner's family never goes to the Union."

Concerning the health of their miners, he observed that "to put our object in the lowest point of view, and to say nothing of humanity or neighbourly feelings, we have a commercial eye to the miner's health with a view to our profit, as well as his advantage . . . Providence Mines are extensive, and we have Winter and Summer underground, but our agents are careful not to allow a man who has worked in the Summer part to go to the Winter part in a strong draught. We change him by degrees, and so his constitution is not subjected to a violent change, but gradually accustom him to different climates . . . In Providence Mines also we don't know what is called the 'Miner's complaint.' This brings me to rather a personal matter. The candles used about here are good candles, and the miner in this district and in St. Just hardly knows what is called Blackspit, which arises, not from powder-smoke, but from impure and bad candles."

Mr. Bevan, mine surgeon, corroborated Mr. Higgs, and said he had seen no case of pulmonary complaint for some years from Providence.

The report by William Hollow and Philip Rogers on the mine, read at this meeting, showed that operations on the Caunter lode had been temporarily suspended, but they were opening E. and W. from it in the 75. On New South lode, the winze sinking below the 75 was worth £12 per fm. and the stope on the cross-course £40. The stope on the Branch was worth £18 per fm. At Hawk's shaft, the lode in the ends at adit level W. was unproductive. Four other cross-cuts were driving in different levels to make discoveries for tin. They were also clearing up some old workings in the western part of the sett. At Little Wheal Speed, the end driving N. in the western carbona was worth £5 per fm.; an improvement was expected in a fathom or two by cutting an E. and W. side lode.

A beautiful new pumping engine, equal to sinking the mine to any depth that might be required, had been purchased from Sandys, Vivian & Co., and was performing splendidly; the cost of this "Copperhouse clock-work" — nearly £1,000 — had been painlessly met by Mr. Higgs quietly stocking "little pinches" of tin each quarter. The winding and stamping engines were both first-class; and by the adoption of wire rope, skips and underground tramways, the cost of discharging the stuff and ore from the mines had been reduced to a little over 2d. a ton. They had 104 men employed on tribute at an average of 9s. 9d. in the £, 100 on tutwork, and 206 men, boys and girls at surface — a total of 410 persons.

Although the falling price of tin cast a slight shadow over this memorable meeting, a good dinner, washed down with generous libations of punch, and an unanticipated dividend of £1 2s. 6d. per share ensured that a thoroughly convivial atmosphere prevailed.[9]

The highest values reported at the December meeting that year were at No. 1 stope in the winze below the 75 on New South lode (£30 per fm.), No. 3 stope (£40) and the branch of lode N. in the 75 (£45.)[10]

In September 1866 a miner named Henry Trevorrow was killed in the 150 fm. level when a large rock fell upon him. The sad event was commemorated in the title poem of R. Hambly's evocative "Down in a Mine (Providence Mines, Lelant, A.D. 1866)" —

We visited one lonely place,

Where but ago a little space,
Huge breaking rocks, with thund'ring sound,
A man stretched lifeless on the ground —
He spoke not, moved not, breathed not more,
His soul had reached th' eternal shore.

At the December meeting a dividend of 10s. per 1,120th share was declared, but their tin was fetching only £47 4s. 6d. per ton, making the outlook uncertain, though the mine maintained its usual promising character.

The agents' report for January 1867 stated that the 75 fm. level in No. 6 carbona was worth £100 per fm. The lode in the deep adit S. was 18″ wide and of a promising character. In April a Penzance newspaper announced that "an extraordinary course of tin," 18′ wide and worth 20s. per barrow (of 22 gallons) had been found in the carbona at the 75, and was so rich that twelve men working on it could pay the entire monthly cost of the mines! The agents' report, issued at the same time, made no mention of this bonanza, although they did describe an improvement in the 65 level, which was worth £20 per fm. However, in September 1868 they announced that No. 6 carbona was worth £100 per fm., whilst No. 7 carbona had very much improved, being worth £60 per fm. The Standard lode in Higgs' shaft, below the 140, was 3′ wide, producing good stones of tin, the granite being of a very congenial character for that metal. The lode in the 85 E. on the Caunter lode was much disturbed. Comfort lode in the 75 S. was 3′ wide, producing good stones of tin. During the October quarter of 1868 85 tons 11 cwt. of tin were sold at an average price of £54 9s. per ton, realising £4,453 19s. 7d. No. 4 carbona was worth £15, No. 5 £20, and No. 6 £100 per fm. The 75 level S. on Comfort lode had improved, being now 7′ wide, with rich stones of tin, and worth £14 per fm. The underground labour force had increased to 220.[12]

Some unusual items of expenditure were listed in July 1869. These included £340 for a 20″ cylinder winding engine, boiler, stamps axle, whim cage, etc.; and £200 for a cargo of oak, required for a new man-engine then being erected on the mine. At this time the setts were renewed for another 21 years. No less than 90 tons of tin were sold that quarter at £71 16s. per ton, and a further 8 tons 7 cwt. at a lower figure, realising altogether £6,871, the profit being £1,766, and the dividend £1 10s. per share. The sum of £50 was presented to the agents, with a vote of thanks for their steady and undivided attention. No. 6 Carbona was worth £75 a fathom, and No. 7 £110.[13]

The man-engine was first put to work in November. It was located on Dunstan's shaft, formerly used as a drawing shaft and more recently as a second ladder-road to the shallower levels. A wood casing extended to a depth of 90 fms., but as this would scarcely have lasted another five years, being in decomposed granite, it was decided to re-line the shaft with stone. The old timber was removed and the shaft built elliptically upwards of massive blocks of surface granite which rested on the hard, solid "country" below, with turned arches at intervals — presumably at the entrances of levels, etc. A double-acting 20″ cylinder engine of 40 h.p., formerly used as a whim at Wheal Margery, was overhauled by Messrs. G. Eustice & Son, and re-erected by them in a new engine-house, which stood adjacent to the main road at Carbis Water. As well as raising men in Dunstan's shaft, this engine could, in emergency, be used as a winder for Higgs' shaft, from which seven-eighths of the stuff being raised from the mine, amounting to a hundred tons daily, was drawn.

The engine was described by A.C. Wildman, of the *Cornish Telegraph,* who rode on it the first day, as follows: "Attached to the outer end of the beam are a sweep rod and crank connected with small wheels, and these again with larger ones. Three revolutions of the engine acting on the larger wheel move the rod twelve feet in the shaft. A huge balance-bob helps up this rod, which is 840′ long, and composed of lengths of Norway balk eight inches square, linked together by iron plates and pins in the usual manner. At the shaft's mouth there is a bracket for your feet at right angles to the rod, with a stout iron bar fastened vertically to the rod, about four feet above the bracket, for holding on by. A wooden shield, on the right, prevents the passenger from stepping off on the wrong side — one always stepped off on the left — and there was another protective shield at his back. After stepping on the bracket, the steam giant above pauses two or three seconds, as if to draw breath and accommodate you. Then, presto! to your left! You are on a substantial sollar, let into one of the interstices in the masonry of the shaft's side. Up goes the rod. Down again. Step in. Down another twelve feet. If you are a good time-ist you are already at home, and can calculate to a nicety, on sollar or bracket, how long you may look about you by candlelight, and observe your surroundings, and when you have to move off and on.

"You are 60 fathoms deep very soon. Long since, the side shield of your platform has been discarded, because, after the first half-dozen descents, you may step right or left in the shaft as you please. Your back is protected all the way down. There is now an underlie north for 30 fathoms, which makes no dfference to you, except that the rollers over which the rods run at this angle creak reproachfully because the engine has not been duly christened, and you have to seize a projecting piece of the iron which here allows the joints play, yet firmly knits them together, instead of the usual iron bar in the rod. At 100 fathoms an excavation appears, made for a huge balance-bob, which aids the rod to rise. Fortunately, tin was found here, and it paid for itself. You are soon after 840′ down, and, declining ladder-work today, go up as easily and safely as you descended."[14]

This man-engine proved a boon by enabling the men to get easily to and from their work, with a great saving of time and toil. The agents said in January 1870 that the miners had worked two hours a day more since its introduction. A total of 500 persons was then employed, 300 of them underground.[15] April saw a valuable improvement in No. 4 Carbona, but it could not be worked to advantage until a cross-cut had been put in at a deeper level. In May, a pare of five miners raised over six tons of tin from a rich bunch they had discovered.[16]

On July 24 1871 members of the Miners' Association of Cornwall and Devonshire paid a visit to the Providence Mines; and the account of this published in their Transactions contains a great deal of valuable information. By that date, total receipts amounted to £530,462 3s. 8d.; the dividends paid without intermission since 1848 totalled £111,020 or more than one-fifth of the expenditure since the beginning in 1832. The hill on which the mines lay was of granite. Underground operations had been carried out on two well-defined lodes and their associated branches. The Standard lode ran nearly due E. and W. and had scarcely any underlie. It had been worked to a depth of 115 fms. below adit, which was itself 50 fms. from surface. Very few men were then working at the bottom, most of the ore being sent up from the 60, 70 and 80 levels. The Caunter lode ran N.E.-S.W., underlying N.W. nearly 3′ in a fathom. It had only been worked to the 80 fm. level. Several branch lodes, to which no names had been given, dipped towards the hill, like the Caunter itself. A lode had been met with at adit level N. of the Standard, and another below, which was productive of tin; it was thought these were portions of the same lode, which in that case would have an underlie S. of 1½′ in the fathom.

The principal features of the mine were the carbonas, which were generally traceable from seams or fissures of the walls of the lodes. Six of these had already been worked on, some being of immense size and remarkable for their rich deposits of tin. This tinstuff consisted mainly of schorl and rock of a granitic character, the tin being only occasionally visible in crystals. The schorl was finely crystallised, whilst the granite varied considerably, some being fine-grained, some like elvans, some coarser and of an open grain, especailly the kind known locally as growan, which was mostly of a greenish-grey colour. The felspar was partially decomposed into chlorite, some being of an orange hue, due to the presence of iron. In some parts of the mine grey chalcedony had been found. About 25 tons of black tin was produced each month, the recovery rate being 2⅛%, or a little higher than the Dolcoath stuff.

The mine had a new dry, fitted with rows of wooden chests to serve as benches for sitting on. The heating was on a new principle, suggested by Capt. Bennetts, of Spearn Moor Mine, which made use of waste steam from the winding engine. This was fed to the boilers of the old dry by a 1½″ steam pipe, only 20 minutes being required to heat the dry to the required temperature. Mr. Higgs, who was responsible for the installation, stated that it did not involve the purchase of one hundredweight of extra coal per week.

There was one 40″ pumping engine which raised water from 150 fms. below adit, and also lifted to surface all water required for the dressing floors. The engine had a 9′ stroke, and normally worked at 4½ strokes per minute; it was equipped with two boilers. This engine was often reported by Mr. Lean as doing more than the average "duty." There was also a winding engine which drew by a wire rope and skip from the engine shaft, this rope passing over a drum and pulley of from 10′-12′ diameter. It possessed an improved arrangement for showing the position of the skip at any moment; this consisted of a screw connected with a shaft of the engine, on which an indicator showed on a graduated plank the position of the skip at the various levels. Connected with the apparatus was a dial with rotary fly, which showed which way the machine was going.

A 30″ engine worked both the stamps and dressing machinery; it had two boilers working at 20-40 lbs. p.s.i. There were two heavy flywheels attached, 24′ and 20′ diameter. The stamps consisted of twelve sets of iron heads, four heads in each set; 100 bushels of stuff was fed to each set in 24 hours.

The man-engine shaft was described, it being mentioned that the cost of the granite lining came to £2 per fathom. The old wood lining had deteriorated through dry rot, caused not by bad ventilation but the nature of the ground. This had also made it necessary to wall and arch with granite one of the adjoining levels for 60 fms. at a similar cost.

The dressing floors were roofed in, enabling work to continue uninterruptedly in wet weather. The manager showed the visitors a buddle considered superior to that of Borlase, which he thought was a modification of those previously in use at Providence. Following a dinner at the account house, Mr. Warington W. Smyth, F.R.S., stated during a speech that Providence was the first mine in Cornwall which adopted the wire rope for winding. Capt. Hollow observed that but for the wire rope and the improved methods of dressing, the mine would have been "knocked" long since.

In September, the breaking of the main rod, piston cap and cylinder cover of the pumping engine caused a serious interruption to the working of the mine. A few weeks afterwards a tributer discovered a valuable lode in a long abandoned old working.[18] January 1872 saw the Standard lode in Higgs' shaft sinking below the 150 by six men, at £160 per ten fathoms. In February, Mr. Higgs conceded the four weeks' month to the miners "before they asked it," a decision which seems to have given general satisfaction. The July account showed the usual favourable sheet, but output was now running at only 66 tons for the quarter, and complaints were made about the high price of coal. The Caunter lode, carbonas and North lode were all productive, and great things were hoped for from the last point.[19] The adventurers resolved in October to surrender the lease of South Providence, under circumstances described in the section on that mine. A carbona branch in the 75 W. of cross-cut was reported worth no less than £200 per fathom.

The shareholders' meeting held on January 7 1873 produced some unpleasant shocks which, in fact signalled the beginning of the end for this great mine. For the first time in 21 years no dividend was paid, the joint pursers explaining this by referring to the heavy drop of £5 14s. per ton in the price received for tin, a fall in output, and increased costs. Another view of the matter was taken by a former shareholder, the highly eccentric Thomas Treweeke, jun., who blamed the present situation on bad management by the pursers (Messrs. S. Higgs & Son) and the agents. In advance of the meeting, he circulated letters and squibs among the shareholders attacking the conduct of these persons; but the meeting unanimously passed a resolution expressing full confidence in their officials. One of the shareholders alleged that Treweeke was motivated by jealousy and spleen, and that he had vainly attempted to get the support of "distant" (non-Cornish) adventurers in his campaign of villification. An interesting item in this account was "Providence & Trelyon United Mine cost £94 3s. 7d."[20]

An unfortunate accident occurred in February 1873 when a sixteen year old youth named John Eddy, disdaining the man-engine, jumped into the skip with his comrade to get to surface more rapidly. When not far from the mouth of the shaft, the lander above heard loud shouting from below, and at once ordered the engine to be stopped. A portion of the wood skipway which had got out of its place had been caught by the skip and forced in on the men, both of whom would have been killed but for the lander's vigilance. As it was, Eddy's legs were badly injured, necessitating the amputation of one of them. He died the following day. Another account says the mishap was caused by a falling roller.[21]

The March account made grim reading, a balance of £1,224 standing against the adventurers, mainly accounted for by a falling off of no less than one third in the returns. The mine then employed 161 men on tutwork and 71 on tribute at an average of 7s. 6d. in the £. A special announcement issued in May stated that "for many years previous to last November, the produce exceeded 20 tons a month; which, with the high price of labour, coals and materials, accounts for the heavy loss; in March, however, the quantity raised was 20 tons, and we hope . . . we shall soon come up to our former position again." The Standard lode had been sunk upon 200 fms. from surface, and was unproductive, the ore being found in shoots and deposits from off the lode.[22]

Another sad accident was reported in September, when two enginemen, Richard Pearce and Emmanuel Prail, were badly scalded by the bursting of a boiler. They were immediately conveyed to their homes; but Prail — the sole support of his widowed mother — died as the cart reached his door, and Pearce on the following day. The management was exonerated from blame, all the customary safety regulations having been strictly enforced, the accident being attributed to lack of "feed" (water) to the pumping engine boiler.[23] Later that month a quarter's loss of £801 was announced, as a result of which the lords were requested to give up dues. In March 1874 most of the tutwork bargains were suspended at the survey and offered to the men on tribute, but not many were reset, the points being poor and generally unremunerative at any price.[24]

Meanwhile, the joint pursers had relinquished their connection with the mine, Mr. S. Higgs, senior, through serious ill health, and his son to take up a mining appointment in Australia. (The latter, according to the *Mining Journal* of September 6 1879, invented and patented an improved process for precipitating copper, using steam.) Following the Higgs' departure, the management of Providence's affairs was entrusted to a committee, but their regime proved a disastrous one. Their terms of reference were, to investigate expenditure, to effect economies, and to confer with the lords about a partial temporary working; but they bungled the job hopelessly. The agents were dismissed, then re-engaged at lower salaries, whilst the mine itself was all but suspended. "A practised hand must surely have concocted the resolution by which the committee was appointed; for whilst marking out their work, a report of which was to be made to the shareholders, for their opinion, it is reasonable to presume, — it concludes, 'and to carry out their own recommendations,' and the latter is evidently the only clause they have read." Most of the best miners had quit, some going to other mines nearby, others leaving the district altogether.[25]

The adventurers held a special meeting later that month under the chairmanship of Mr. R.H. Bamfield to appoint a new purser following the death of Samuel Higgs, senior. They placed on record their sense of loss at his passing after a connection of nearly forty years with the mine, and appointed Edward Trythall as his successor.[26] The June account showed an appalling loss of £2,082, to meet which a call of £2 was levied. Trythall disclosed that during the last four weeks of the quarter they had stopped raising tin because of the prevailing low price, but production had since been resumed.[27]

The October account showed some gleams of hope, no call being required, and the book nearly balanced, but the general outlook remained depressing. Reference was made to 36 relinquished shares; whilst the labour force had been reduced to 52 tributers and 57 tutworkers — a total of only 109 underground. Capt. Hollow stated that he and Capt. Rogers now had to do the work formerly entrusted to four agents.[28] In November, several of the principal tribute pitches were reported to have fallen off in value, but an improvement in Hawk's shaft would compensate for this. However, the lode here was heaved by flookans crossing the Standard lode. They were confident of finding the lode again, as at Higgs' shaft it had been recovered after being hove 14 fms., while at Hawk's they had only driven 8 fms. for it.

A very small profit (£148 19s. 6d.) was shown at the account for January 1875. The lords — somewhat tardily — had given up dues during pleasure to assist in developing the mine. In the following twelve months Providence sold 147 tons 6 cwt. of tin at an average price of £49 8s. 10d. a ton. In January 1876 Hawk's shaft was complete to the 65 fm. level; the skip-road was fixed and plat cut, and sinking would shortly be resumed. There were 36 tributers working in that part of the mine, the total labour force being 48 on tut, 64 on tribute, with 30 men and 63 females and boys at surface — 205 altogether.[29] The April account showed a greatly worsened situation. The loss on four months' working amounted to £775 6s. 5d., the total unfavourable balance being £1,339 8s. 7d., to meet which a call of £1 per 1120th share was made. The loss was partly attributable to the low price of tin — £42 a ton, or £6 5s. a ton less than at the previous account, and £22 per ton below the average price of all the tin sold from the mine, extending over a period of 44 years.

"£40 7s. 6d. is the lowest price Providence Mines have received for tin since 1844!"

Purser Trythall and the agents put up a gallant fight to save the mine as tin prices fell still further during the next eighteen moinths, but all to no avail; and in November 1877 the Providence Mines were offered for sale by auction as a going concern. Not surprisingly, no bids were made; and the mines were thereupon offered to the lords in accordance with the terms of the setts, but they declined the option. Underground operations were then suspended, and work began on stripping the property. In December, two tin tribute pitches were still working in the back of the 75 fm. level E. of Higgs' shaft in No. 3 Carbona by six men at 13s. 4d. in the £. Tin would be returned from these pitches and leavings as long as the stamping engine remained unsold.[30] Since 1832, about £533,000 worth of tin and £58,000 worth of copper had been sold, whilst £113,000 had been paid in dividends, against £23,000 called up.

The materials offered for sale in January 1878 included the 40″ pumping engine, 9′ stroke, with two 11 ton boilers; 20″ stamping engine, 9′ and 8′ stroke, with two boilers, 19 tons; two fly-wheels and wrought-iron shafts, and two stamps' axles for 32 heads; 23″ winding engine, double-acting, 6′ stroke, with two boilers, 10 tons and 8 tons, and whim-cage; 20″ man-engine, double-acting, 6′ stroke, with fly-wheel, two wrought-iron shafts, 8 tons boiler, and balance bob; a heavy 10′ diameter toothwheel; an 8″ horizontal engine, 20″ stroke; six pulverisers; calciner and water wheel; several other water wheels; "also the rich tin leavings throughout the mine, the accumulation of many years, during the greater part of which this has been one of the greatest tin producing mines in the county."[31] The final pay-day took place that same month — a melancholy affair, and merely a shadow of what it had been when these mines circulated £1,100 a month in wages. Most of the young men who worked there had emigrated, the older ones could find no work.

It appears that the auction was unsuccessful, doubtless owing to the current mining depression; it had to be re-advertised in February; and as late as December the three largest engines and other equipment still lay on the site unsold.[32] The final winding-up of its affairs did not take place till a year later, when a dividend of £1 2s. 6d. per share was distributed out of realised assets.[33]

In 1906 one of the shafts of Wheal Providence collapsed in a spectacular fashion. The *St. Ives Weekly Summary* of November 24 reported that the wooden sollar which had been fixed in the shaft 10 or 15 ft. from surface and covered with many tons of stones and earth when the mine closed, gave way during the night, carrying with it a large portion of the garden at the rear of Carbis Bay Post Office, together with about 70 feet of a newly built wall. About ten feet from the shaft lay the workshop of Mr. T.R. Glasson, builder, whose employees had been constantly walking over it, unaware of its existence. The shaft was 110 fms. in depth; and the large quantity of rubbish falling into it drove the water out of the adit with such force that it completely flooded Carbis Valley and Mr. John Williams' private residence and picnic grounds.

Although the *Summary* described the collapse as being of "an apparently unknown shaft, in connection with Wheal Providence mine," it seems possible that the shaft may, in fact, have belonged to the closely adjoining East Providence, whose workings partly lay within Carbis Valley.

At around this period a general revival was taking place in Cornish mining; and in November 1906 Frederick Rouse Pool, of the Cornish Hand Wrought Metal Co., and C. Ranger-Gull, a well-known author, who held an option on Providence, concluded negotiations with the Tasmanian Exploration Co., of London, for its re-working. Inspired by this success, Ranger-Gull announced his intention to write a novel about Cornish mining under the pen-name of Guy Thorne. A few weeks later Mr. M. Rhys Jones, Chairman of the Tasmanian Exploration Co. Ltd., visited the mine, and was favourably impressed by its large size — the setts covered 720 acres — and rich development potential. He described the workings as fairly dry, but something like 15,000,000 gallons of water had accumulated in them since the suspension. Orders were placed for pumping equipment before the end of that year; and in June 1907 it was reported that stamps were being erected.[34]

This stamps battery was put in to deal with some shallow tin-bearing ground discovered above water level before pumping commenced. The adit was cleared from the sea to Dunstan's shaft, leaving about 50 fms. to be dealt with up to the main (Higgs' Sump) shaft which was found to be filled in to a depth of 9 fms. When it had been cleared and timbered to the sollar, they discovered that, 8 fms. below the sollar, the timbering of the sides had failed, resulting in a complete collapse. The shaft, which measured 12′ by 7′, was reinstated to adit level (50 fms.) Owing to its troublesome nature, this undertaking entailed five months of very hard work, over a thousand tons of debris having to be taken out, which was completed by the end of June.

It was intended that Higgs' shaft should form the central working shaft of the combined setts. In the western part of the property Carninney or Little Wheal Speed shaft had been opened up. It was 70 fms. deep and connected with the main workings, but was also found in a collapsed state. This was cleared to adit level, here 58 fms. from surface. Two rich tin lodes lay in this section which had been opened up and worked on by tributers since the closing of the mine, but this had been stopped by the shaft's collapse. The shaft was equipped with a small winding engine, and tin ore, assaying above the average, was being raised there. An adjoining shaft, 60 fms. deep, giving access to the same ground, had also been restored and equipped with a ladderway.

Wheal Hawk shaft, near the northern boundary, had been filled in; they cleared it to a sollar 20 fms. from surface, installed a small steam pump and unwatered it to the 14 fm. level. A small winding plant and a skipway were also placed in this shaft. This was believed to be an important section, as at the time of closing rich ground was being explored here. Wheal Hawk was connected with the main workings at adit level, this level now being cleared towards Higgs'.

At surface, the usual workshops and offices were being erected. The dry was described as "novel," the men's clothes being aired in a hot air chamber, as in a laundry, so avoiding contamination of the atmosphere in the dry itself. Hot air was provided by exhaust steam from the fitting shop engine.

Frazer & Chalmer, of London, were erecting 20 heads of Californian stamps, the first unit of which (10 heads) would deal with 35-40 tons of stuff per day. The output from these would be treated by Record, Wilfley, and Frue Vanner tables, classifying into four sizes instead of the usual three. Nearly two acres of rough ground were being cleared for erecting a tin house, calciner and slime frames. The main milling plant would be driven by a 200 h.p. Cross compound condensing engine, with reserve power for the second section of stamps as well as an Ingersoll belt-driven compressor until such time as the whole power of the engine might be required for the battery, when the compressor would be given its own power plant. They were already treating the dumps, which were valuable, one enormous burrow being valued at £40,000 for tin. Towards the sea lay the mine's copper section, which would be developed as soon as the tin part was in working order. Mr. F. Rouse Pool was manager of the undertaking, assisted by Mr. James Bickle, engineer, of Camborne. The labour force totalled 157 men.[35]

In August, one of Evans' steam pumps, weighing with chains 12 tons, and having a steam cylinder and a ram respectively 16″ and 8″ in diameter, able to deliver 13,500 gallons per hour against a pressure head of 60′, was lowered into Higgs' shaft. When fully equipped it would weigh 25 tons. Mr. J.R. Daniel, of Camborne, in a speech on this occasion, said the development work had gone ahead rapidly, despite the unexpectedly high cost and difficulty of shaft clearance. Stuff raised from all parts of the mine would go to one large tipping table, then pass into the rock-breaker, fall into a bucket elevator, and be automatically carried up to a bin. From here it would proceed to the stamps. The whole process would be automatic, only six workers being required, whereas in the old days from 80 to 90 were employed on the dressing floors.[36]

A serious setback occurred during November, when the offices, carpenters' shop, changing house and sampling house were destroyed in a disastrous fire, together with the clothes of the afternoon and night men. Not long afterwards operations were totally suspended. In 1912 it was stated that Providence Tin Mines, Ltd., had spent £30,000 on development work, but shortage of capital brought the venture to a premature close. In 1912 the Lelant (Cornwall) Exploration Syndicate, Ltd., proposed to set up a "large" company with a capital of £25,000 to rework the property. Criticism was expressed that such a sum would prove quite inadequate to restart so large a mine whose prospects, nevertheless, were considered excellent.[37] This view, apparently, was shared by investors; and in January 1916 it was reported that Providence had been dismantled.

1. *Royal Cornwall Gazette* 1810
2. *Royal Cornwall Gazette* May 1810
3. *Royal Cornwall Gazette* February 1815

4. *Royal Cornwall Gazette* February 5 1847
5. *Cornish Telegraph* November 25 1856
6. *Cornish Telegraph* July 14 1858
7. *Cornish Telegraph* November 30 1859
8. *Cornish Telegraph* September 2 1863
9. *Royal Cornwall Gazette* May 24 and June 2 1865
10. *Royal Cornwall Gazette* December 7 1865
11. *Royal Cornwall Gazette* December 6 1866
12. *Cornish Telegraph* October 7 1868
13. *Cornish Telegraph* July 7 1869
14. *Cornish Telegraph* December 1 1869
15. *Cornish Telegraph* January 5 1870
16. *Cornish Telegraph* May 18 1870
17. *Cornish Telegraph* April 5 1871
18. *Cornish Telegraph* November 1 1871
19. *Cornish Telegraph* July 3 1872
20. *Cornish Telegraph* January 8 1873
21. *Cornish Telegraph* February 19 1873
22. *Cornish Telegraph* May 14 1873
23. *Cornish Telegraph* September 3 1873
24. *Cornish Telegraph* March 18 1874
25. *Cornish Telegraph* May 12 1874
26. *Cornish Telegraph* May 27 1874
27. *Cornish Telegraph* July 1 1874
28. *Cornish Telegraph* October 14 1874
29. *Cornish Telegraph* January 6 1876
30. *Cornish Telegraph* September 11 and 25 and December 4 1877
31. *Cornish Telegraph* January 8 1878
32. *Cornish Telegraph* December 24 1878
33. *Cornish Telegraph* January 1 1880
34. *Western Echo* November 17 1906; January 19 and February 9 1907
35. *Western Echo* June 29 1907
36. *Western Echo* August 31 1907
37. *Western Echo* December 14 1912

EAST PROVIDENCE

As its name implies, this mine adjoins Providence on the East, and exploits the same run of lodes. Its workings extend from the old hamlet of Carbis Water, at the head of Carbis Valley, to the south-eastern cliffs of Carbis Bay (Porthrepta) Beach, embracing the southern side of that valley and the area around the railway station. East Providence, indeed, occupied a most beautiful site overlooking a singularly attractive wooded valley and a then unspoilt coastline; and several visitors to this district in the mid-19th century wrote admiringly of its charming situation and picturesque appearance. The principal shafts were Boorman's (20 yards S. of the former Methodist Chapel at Carbis Water), Carbona (230 yards E. by S. of the chapel), Harvey's (120 yards S. of the station) and Pool's (20 yards N. of the station). Two adits are still to be seen in the cliffs on the S.E. side of the beach, one of which appears to have been a trial only, but the other leads to a shaft.

East Providence is of considerable antiquity, but no records are known of its early workings. The sett was taken up by a London company in 1857 who prosecuted it vigorously for a number of years, encouraged by the success of its prosperous neighbour, but the results, financially, at least, proved consistently disappointing. At a meeting held on March 6 1857, Mr. N. Harvey in the chair, it was resolved that the mine be divided into 2,048 shares. Mr. James Hollow was appointed purser, and Mr. Hollow, sen., agent.[1] In November 1860 the adventurers were cheered by the news that the rich Providence South lode had been cut; it was in granite, and had every appearance of being a first-rate discovery.[2] However, this brought no relief from calls; and in March 1861 the adverse balance stood at nearly £1,000. Capt. T. Richards was then appointed manager at £2 2s. per month.[3]

In 1864, Boorman's shaft, 12′ long by 5′ wide, was reported 70 fms. deep. It was used for pumping and winding, and underlay 5′ per fm. The 70 fm. level was driving by 6 men about 10 fms. from the shaft. The 60 fm. level had been driven 18 fms. to the new lode, which it had gone through, and was still driving by 6 men. New lode was driving E. by 4 men, being advanced 15′, whilst the western end was advanced 6′, driving by two men. A winze sinking by 6 men was nearly through to the 70. The 40 fm. level was driving towards Wilson's shaft, which was being sunk from surface by 6 men; it lay 45 fms. from Boorman's. The 30 fm. level had been driven from Boorman's to under Wilson's, and a bore hole had just been put through. The men changed over the boiler, which had two feed cocks, and was worked at low pressure.[4]

In 1865 a Mr. Edward Cooke complained that he had been induced to buy heavily into the mine at a high price by the flattering reports of the agents which had not been borne out by results, yet he still had faith in her. The management seems to have been reorganised at about this time, and Henry Paull, M.P., who fought and won a very strenuous Parliamentary contest at St. Ives that year became associated with it, doubtless for political reasons. During a meeting at the London Tavern in October, Capt. Nancarrow of St. Ives Consols was appointed manager, and a new management committee elected—the second in two months—consisting of Messrs. Phillips, Rawlings, Harvey & Co., and R.H. Bamfield. Reference was made to an improvement in the shaft. Capt. Teague (of Tincroft) had reported most favourably on the mine. Their basic object was to reach the same lodes that were so productive in Providence; and present indications justified the hope that this would be realised.[5]

In March 1866 the agents—J. Nancarrow and W. White—reported the lode in the 50 E. of Boorman's 1′ wide, worth £5 per fm. The 60 end E. was worth £4 per fm., while the lode in the 82 E. was 2′ wide, with promising appearance and yielding tin to save.[6] Their report for May was extremely detailed and of an encouraging nature. Boorman's shaft had been cased and divided, a skip road put in to the 82 fm. level, and a plat cut at the 82. The shaft was now sinking 2 fms. below the level by 6 men and 3 boys, the lode 2′ wide. The 82 was driven 4 fms. E. of Boorman's, lode 4′ wide, yielding good stones of tin. This level had been driven 28 fms. E. of Boorman's, where the lode was not very valuable, but an improvement could be expected. The rise above this level had been communicated with the 60 driven 60 fms. E. of Boorman's but suspended until ventilated by communication with the levels above or below. There was tin ground in the end of this level, where the lode seemed disordered by a crossing. The 50 was driven 28 fms. E. of Boorman's, the last 8 fms. through ground worth £5-6 per fm. The Caunter lode in the 60 E. was poor, and its driving had been suspended.

The ground in Boorman's shaft was favourable for sinking, and they expected to make good progress towards another level by the end of the quarter. The rough weather had greatly interfered with surface operations, but the stamps were now being erected. Although tin worth £446 19s. 5d. had been sold to Daubuz & Co. and Michell & Co., a debit balance of £268 17s. 8d. was incurred and a call of 2s. 6d. made. The Chairman (Mr. T. Hollow) congratulated the adventurers on the satisfactory state of the mine, and Capt. Nancarrow stated that the underground workings never looked better, for the deeper they went the greater was the improvement, and he believed that when a deeper point had been reached they would have a really good mine. A rather chilling note was, however, struck by Mr. Bamfield, one of the committee, who disclosed that £150 was owed in unpaid calls, and that petitions had been filed against four defaulting shareholders.[7]

An interesting description of the machinery was published in August. "Between the account house and the sea is the pumping engine, a very good one of 40″ cylinder, erected at a cost of about £1,500, and doing its work very easily, for with a 5′ lift to the 40, a few strokes per minute keep the mine clear of water, the hornblende schist which the shaft penetrates being dry. Towards St. Ives is a new stamping and winding engine, designed by Messrs. Eustice & Son of Hayle, and constructed by Messrs. Harvey of the same place. It is well worth the visit we pay it—so bright and clean is the machinery, so easy the movement, and yet so firm the way in which the hard work is done. It is a 24″ cylinder, does all the necessary winding, and is at present turning very briskly 16 heads of stamps. These could be easily increased to 32. Until within the last three months it was necessary to convey all tin-stuff to the Stennack, near St. Ives, the carriage to which place was 32s. per 100 sacks, besides the rent of stamps. The saving of this makes a nice little set-off to the interest on the expenditure on this very pretty little engine. It is capable of returning 20 tons of tin a month."

That part of East Providence lying nearest the sea which had been partially explored for copper was now temporarily abandoned for the section adjoining Providence, where Boorman's shaft had been sunk to try to strike the productive lodes going E. which, once found, might be followed to Trevethoe Plantation. This shaft had now reached a depth of 94 fms. and the lode looked better than anywhere else below the 82. In the 70 E. of this shaft a valuable discovery had been made in a winze going down to the 82, where a carbona-like formation had been found going N.E., worth from £12-15 per fm. As further evidence of the mine's richness, it was mentioned that, at another place, a man and boy who had worked laboriously for months for very poor returns, suddenly struck rich pay ground, and extracted 21 cwt. of tin in 28 days, for which they received £24 on the following pay day.

East Providence was now extracting one ton of tin from every 35 tons of stuff stamped; at the neighbouring Providence Mines 120 tons of stuff were stamped each day, giving one ton of tin. The metal raised during the past year was claimed to be as rich as, perhaps, richer, than any in the district; and 517 sacks had recently yielded more than 5 tons of tin. 16 tribute pitches were working by 35 men at an average tribute of 11s. in the £.[8]

In November 1867 John Nancarrow and William White reported Boorman's shaft sunk 9½ fms. below the 94. There had been little lode for the last 4 or 5 fms. sinking, but it was now forming again at the bottom of the shaft. The 94 level was driven 13 fms. E. of Boorman's. The 82 had been driven 53 fms. E., where there was a large and promising lode. The carbona below the 70 E. had recently improved, being now worth £9 per fm. The rise above the 70 E. was up to 5½ fms. and should be holed by the end of the month. The shallow level for draining off the water was nearly finished.

Mr. Phillips, one of the principal shareholders, put several searching questions to Capt. Nancarrow regarding the state of the mine, with which he appeared to be not wholly satisfied. In reply to his final query, "Is it worth while to go on with the mine; you would not abandon her?" Capt. Nancarrow replied, "Certainly not, sir, or you will leave to some one else the reward for all your own toil and outlay."[9]

The mine continued to lose money over the next few years, and matters reached a crisis in August 1868 when the representatives of a large shareholder who had died (Phillips) would neither relinquish his shares (on which calls were due) or pay the outstanding amount. The other shareholders demanded that they should quickly decide which course to adopt. Capts. Nancarrow and White reported that the carbona in the 94 had not answered expectations, the tinstuff raised being of poor quality, but it looked well as they drove eastward, and a deposit of tin was hoped for at its junction with the Standard lode, about 6 fms. before the end.

There was also a good looking tinny lode gone down below the level. The 106 was being pushed on eastward as fast as possible by six men; they still had 20 fms. to drive to get under the carbona. Boorman's shaft was 11 fms. below the 106, sinking by nine men and three boys. Every effort was being made to get down this shaft, believing that success would come with depth, as in the adjoining mine. There were thirteen pitches working by 25 men, at an average tribute of 11s. 3d. in the £; 31 men and boys were on tutwork; and altogether 80 hands employed.

About six months would be required in getting at the junction of the carbona and the Standard lode, and to get the 106 eastward, to prove the ground under the carbona. Capt. Nancarrow explained that such a carbona in Providence or St. Ives Consols, or any mine in the neighbourhood, would in all probability have been much richer. Nearly all their expense was being incurred underground, their engine-men, landers, smiths, etc., numbering only about a dozen, and no effort would be spared to work the mine in an economical way. "The usual cheering dinner was enjoyed, the Purser, Mr. T. Hollow, in the chair. Soon afterwards Mrs. Paull, and some ladies who were enjoying a ramble on the cliffs, were invited to the Count-house to taste a glass of the fragrant punch, in doing which they wished the speculation success."[10]

At the November meeting, it was announced that the late Mr. Phillips' estate having proved insolvent, it had been decided to resolve the matter by taking the shares into the company. Despite this, and the usual call, the purser was in cheerful mood, as tin sales had increased during the quarter, and the prospects had distinctly improved. The lode in the 96 and 106 was looking well and had been valued at from £8-10 per fm. The nature of the new lode in the bottom level was precisely the same as the Providence Caunter lode at the same depth at which that mine made its great discoveries, and was no doubt the point where for some years past the agents had anticipated good results.[11]

Although a small call was made at the February 1869 meeting, the agents' report was encouraging, and the adventurers passed a vote of thanks to Purser Hollow for his "correct management" of the mine. Then, in October, a circular was issued informing the shareholders that the lode had been cut in the bottom of Boorman's shaft. It would take the rest of the month to cut through and open on it, and until then its value could not be ascertained. It was nevertheless regarded as an important discovery. The lode in the 122 was 2' wide, of a very encouraging nature, and producing good tin. The 106 had also improved, and was yielding tin.[10]

On learning this news, A.C. Wildman, editor of the *Cornish Telegraph,* and one of the best mining journalists of the period, hastened to the mine to see the discovery for himself. He wrote a detailed account of his visit, which gives an excellent idea of the manner in which this adventure was then being conducted.

Journeying to the mine by rail to St. Ives Road station and from thence by trap—the branch line had not then been constructed—he was greeted by "a bob which bows you a stately welcome", and entertained to dinner at the account house. The visitor was then conducted to the changing house and supplied with underground attire, candles, and a ball of St. Agnes clay. While this was going on, his guide, Cap'n Will, in a whispered aside to the purser, promised he would give the stranger "a sweater" on the ladders—a promise which, Wildman ruefully acknowledged, was faithfully fulfilled! However, their descent did not begin immediately. "I thought that our underground path was close to the polite engine which nodded us a welcome, but was soon undeceived. We had to traverse the circuitous, up-hill, cinder-made road which leads from the mine to the main thoroughfare from Hayle to St. Ives. This was followed for some distance; and a stile on the left, and a private road soon brought us up to the very outworks of the mine's rich neighbour, our old and much esteemed friend, Providence. These defences were walls of Cyclopean masonry, which served to keep together the huge burrows from which considerably more than half a million of money has been extracted.''

They entered the mine by a ''hole'' covered by a rude shed, through which the breezes blew keenly. In this shed they made an inspection of the first barrowful of ore from the newly discovered lode—a dull red material in which tiny crystals of tin could be seen glistening brightly. Descending a short ladder they reached a sollar, then passed through another hole and down a perpendicular ladder to a second sollar, shrouded in dim twilight. As they descended still further, leaving all daylight behind, Cap'n Will explained that the shaft was cut down through hard ground, and, except for the casing on the left which afforded protection from moving skips, and in the sollars, there was very little timber. Cap'n Will was proud of the fact that in all the years he had worked there, there had never been an accident, and drew attention to the ladder-work—''although a calling mine, we have all, above and below, in excellent order.''

The engine down on the cliff sent ''a tremendously long arm, called a flat rod, a furlong up the hill and inland to this shaft, and close to us, in the ladder-way, eight feet up and down, with a rush and clank as if fifty giants shook their manacles, the huge pump rods work.'' At some levels a square iron box rose and fell into a slightly larger box to send air into the more distant parts of the mine. This engine-rod sometimes ran close to the ladders, and the visitor was enjoined to keep his elbows in, to avoid contact with it. From the other side of the casing was heard the rumbling of the skip; ''so that, between clank and gurgle, rattle and hiss, there is sound enough and to spare.''

For the first twenty fathoms the sides of the shaft were dry and a cold air rushed upwards. Below this, the wet oozed from the shaft's sides, the rungs of the ladder were coated with slippery mud, and the air grew warm and oppressive. They then entered a stiff underlie where the tediousness of the less perpendicular descent was aggravated by the half-stooping position required to accommodate hands and feet to the staves. So, at last, they reached the 122 fm. sump, or place where the lowest pump rod reached. Here was a substantial winch, with a man and a boy on the handles. ''Sixty-six feet down a lower pit—the continuation of the shaft—a light is seen. To reach it, a ladder goes down some distance, and a chain is the last link of communication from the base of this ladder to the very bottom of the mine. With many a hollow-sounding bang from side to side of the shaft, up comes a sixteen-gallon kibble, full of water, which is emptied into the sump.''

Not liking the look of this last hole, Wildman decided to descend no further, but to examine the lode where it could be most easily inspected, in the 122. ''We turn round in this, the most cavernous part of the mine we have yet seen, and try to illumine the gloom by holding aloft the candles. Dark are its recesses; Rembrandt-like the shadows and the dim lights which fall on the brown faces and figures of the miners. We turn into a level—a tunnel a foot higher than a tall man and of ample width

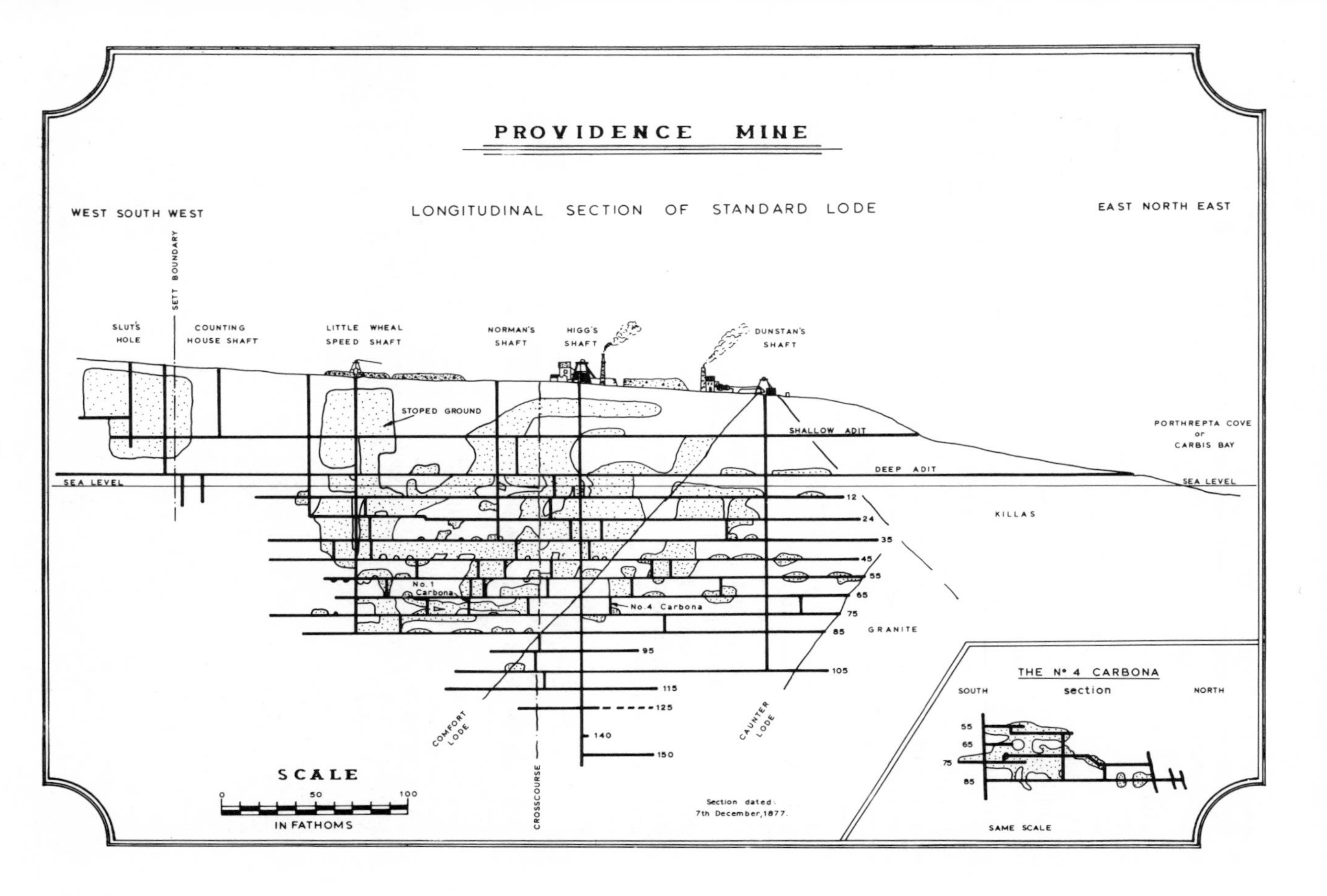

PROVIDENCE MINE
LONGITUDINAL SECTION OF STANDARD LODE
WEST SOUTH WEST
EAST NORTH EAST
SETT BOUNDARY
SLUT'S HOLE
COUNTING HOUSE SHAFT
LITTLE WHEAL SPEED SHAFT
NORMAN'S SHAFT
HIGG'S SHAFT
DUNSTAN'S SHAFT
STOPED GROUND
SHALLOW ADIT
PORTHREPTA COVE or CARBIS BAY
DEEP ADIT
SEA LEVEL
SEA LEVEL
KILLAS
12
24
35
45
55
65
75
85
GRANITE
No. 1 Carbona
No.4 Carbona
95
105
115
125
140
150
COMFORT LODE
CROSSCOURSE
CAUNTER LODE
SCALE
0
50
100
IN FATHOMS
Section dated: 7th December, 1877.
THE No 4 CARBONA section
SOUTH
NORTH
55
65
75
85
SAME SCALE

for the most brawny shoulders. A plank is our carpet, to keep the feet from the mud, and over this we walk ten fathoms, turn at an angle, and get over twelve fathoms more, and the long-sought lode is before us.

"We have had so many turns and twists, that whether we look north, south, east or west, I know not. I am told that this lode runs parallel to the rich veins of our wealthy neighbour; what I see is this:—On each side, walls of granite, which, when you think of the weight they bear, seem to threaten instant death to the pigmies who have attacked them. In front, a clearly-defined lode, sloping from your extended right hand towards the left foot—a huge sandwich, placed on end and held diagonally, the bread and butter of unknown thickness, the meat, the lode before us, from 2½′ to 4′ thick. It is richest towards the feet; so down on his knees goes one of the two miners who are at work on it, to dig out a morsel for the stranger. But specimens don't come at a moment's notice, and half-an-hour is spent before a bit, much richer than the rest, can be secured. The end is warmish, and having again surveyed the lode with an earnest hope that it may prove of solid and durable value, and having once more witnessed the toilsome work of winding up that kibble full of water, we talk of going up.

"If coming down made the limbs ache, caused you to perspire, and was done with many a long-drawn breath, what will the ascent be? Well worthy of attainment, the goal can only be won little by little, and by perseverance; and the blessed sunshine and fresh air are worth toiling for. A benediction on the man-engine, say I. It would take me, by stepping from one piece of wood to another, in successive jerks, to the surface with ninety steps; now, the weight of the body has to be lifted, a foot high, seven hundred and thirty times. One drink from the miner's little can of water, and off we start." So, painfully the ascent was made, with a stop half-way to get their breath back. At last the pin's head of blue sky was seen above, and after another effort they finally reached surface, to be refreshed by a few grapes and a cup of tea laced by Cognac—"the purser's prescription"—at the account house.[13]

Unhappily, the prosperity which seemed to be promised by this lode was not fulfilled; and the dismal succession of continuing calls led to the mine being closed in 1871. The materials auctioned in November included the 40″ pumping engine with 11 tons boiler; and the 24″ winding and stamping engine, with 10 tons boiler, axle and 16 heads of stamps.[14]

After East Providence closed, Mr. William Payne rented the site, which he converted into a number of fields; he also demolished the old mine chimney and converted the engine house with its 3′-4′ thick walls into a cottage, where he resided. With the opening of the branch railway in 1877 he bought the land and laid it out as tea gardens and picnic grounds, whilst the former engine pool became a boating lake. As Carbis Bay developed Mr. Payne built a new house for himself, giving the old one to his eldest son, and also established a large assembly room which for nearly 70 years served for dances, roller skating and also for church services prior to the building of Carbis Bay parish church. His old house later became part of the Cottage Hotel, where an extensive scheme of modernisation was completed as recently as 1979; the old engine pond and boating lake now serves as a full sized swimming pool for its guests.[15]

In this fashion was Carbis Valley transformed from a great centre of mining to meet the requirements of the modern tourist industry; whilst Carrack Gladden Cove, once stained red with water from the stamps, was developed by Mr. John Payne and others into one of the district's most popular bathing beaches.

1. *Cornish Telegraph* March 11 1857
2. *Cornish Telegraph* November 14 1860
3. *Cornish Telegraph* March 26 1861
4. Report, Lord Kinnaird's Royal Commission into Conditions of Mines, 1864
5. *Royal Cornwall Gazette* September 8 and November 2 1865
6. *Cornish Telegraph* March 7 1866
7. *Cornish Telegraph* May 9 1866
8. *Cornish Telegraph* November 14 1866
9. *Cornish Telegraph* August 21 1867
10. *Cornish Telegraph* August 26 1868
11. *Cornish Telegraph* December 2 1868
12. *Cornish Telegraph* October 20 1869
13. *Cornish Telegraph* November 3 1869
14. *Cornish Telegraph* November 15 1871. The settling of the mine's affairs took some time to complete. A final call of 10s. 6d. was made on the contributories through the Vice-Warden's Court in January 1874
15. *Western Morning News* September 26 1968

SOUTH WHEAL PROVIDENCE (SOUTH WHEAL SPEED, ADELAIDE)

As indicated by its name, this mine adjoins Providence on the S., the sett embracing the tenements of Trewartha, Boskerris Wartha, and Laity. The actual workings lay a little to the E. of Boskerris Wartha, and the old account house (now a country club) is situated just N. of Laity Lane. Its first phase of working seems to have taken place under the name of Adelaide. The *Royal Cornwall Gazette* of July 23 1831 carried an advertisement inviting merchants "disposed to supply Wheal Elizabeth Mine, situate in the parish of St. Erth, and Wheal Adelaide Mine, in the parish of Lelant . . . with the undermentioned Articles," which included timber, coal, candles, tallow, gunpowder, quills, pickhilts, shovels and sieves.

As South Wheal Speed, the mine produced 55 tons of black tin and a little copper between 1852-5. As South Wheal Providence it raised 80 tons of black tin between 1855-82, 4 tons 13 cwt. 3 qrs. being sold in 1856 for £247. In the summer of that year it was reported to be working at a profit, and had an 80″ steam engine—a large machine for such a small mine, possibly indicating a misprint. Samuel Higgs was then the purser and Capt. Richard James the manager; the adventure was in 100 shares, £22 10s. paid (£28 10s. paid in 1857.) In November 1857 the materials were offered for sale by auction. They included a capstan, shears, pumps, a horse whim, flat rods, 100 fms. of ladders, and tools, "the workings of the above mine having ceased."

Some years afterwards the sett of South Providence was granted to the adjoining Providence Mines, who, however, failed to develop it to the lord's satisfaction. The following passage, taken from a Providence Mines report dated October 7 1872 has a bearing on this matter:

"Mr. Glanville has sent a letter on behalf of Mr. Tyringham, in reference to South Providence Mine, in which he writes that Mr. Praed states: 'If you are not prepared to erect an engine and thoroughly develop the ground, he shall feel it incumbent on him, in the interest of the property, to determine the sett.' The facts of the case are, that we erected a powerful new engine at the Providence Mines at a very heavy cost, with a view of working this addition to the sett; our object was to discover a lode and to sink a shaft to open the district. We have driven levels South of our Providence sett at a cost of many thousand pounds in search of, but found no lode worth prosecuting; we never had any thought of working that part of our sett in which an engine had previously been erected. The above matter having been taken into consideration, it was resolved that the sett of South Providence Mine be surrendered at Christmas next."[1]

In 1906 Mr. P.E. de Mattos, who was then privately working Worvas Downs mine with Lord Armstrong, took up the lease of South Providence and at once began to unwater it. Lodes trending S.E. were known to exist there, and also one or two cross lodes. The workings were not very deep, the bottoms being 80 fms. from surface, but old miners spoke very highly of the property.[2] In September of the following year good progress was reported at South Providence. The mine was being drained by one of Evans' steam pumps, a depth of 80 fms. having been reached—presumably the bottom, or very near it. A shaft which communicated with the pumping shaft at the 50 fm. level had been equipped for winding, and a ladderway shaft between them put in order. The "cavities" (? stopes) underlay N. 75 deg. on the principal E. and W. lode, which was productive of copper as well as tin. It had been decided to sink the main shaft considerably deeper, and to extend the upper and lower levels to the Comfort lode, struck during the former working at the 60 fm. level, and then, by driving S. on this lode, attempt to intersect another one running parallel with the main lode. By then, a large amount of good new ground should have been opened up for stoping. There were five known E. and W. lodes, besides one running N. and S., and all indications pointed to the sett, which had been but very partially developed, being well mineralised. About 80 men were employed here, and at Worvas Downs. Capt. Trevorrow, of St. Ives, was the underground foreman.[3] This working appears to have been very short-lived.

1. *Cornish Telegraph* October 2 1872
2. *Western Echo* July 7 1906
3. *Western Echo* September 26 1907

Other references:
Kelly 1856 p. xxxv

MJ 1857 (31.10), 1886 (6.3)
Murchison 1856 p. 68
Tredinnick 1857 p. 121
Dines 1956 p. 125

PROVIDENCE UNITED

There is a record of a mine of this name, in Lelant, selling 17 tons of black tin in 1885. Location unknown.

WHEAL REETH

This ancient mine lies on the southern flank of Trink Hill, near the western border of Lelant parish, where it adjoins Towednack, and seems originally to have borne the name of the hill itself. In a case mentioned in *Proceedings in Chancery in the Reign of Elizabeth* (vol. 3, p. 136, No. 15) Edward Trevalscus (plaintiff) claimed from Pascoe Kerne (defendant) relief against a mortgage on "a messuage and land with a tin mine called Trerinke alias Trefinke in the parish of Uny Lavant." The designation "Reeth" must have come in at a slightly later period, but before the Cornish language had become extinct in the area. This name means "red," and was bestowed on a number of other mines in West Cornwall, doubtless in allusion to the colour of their lode material. Mr. Justin Brooke has found a reference to one in Breage before 1728 and to another in St. Just from 1822, whilst Wheal Reeth Bounds were recorded in St. Just as early as 1665. There was also a Reeth in Germoe, adjoining Great Work; this was active in the 1930's, much of the capital being put up by the Simpsons, of Penzance, outfitters. Occasionally the spelling "Reath" is preferred, and it is sometimes even given as "Wreath", the latter obviously arising from a misunderstanding of its meaning.

Wheal Reeth was worked on a large scale at an earlier period than any other mine in the district. In 1748 a "fire engine" was employed to drain the workings, a clear indication that the enterprise was already showing promise of the great riches which were later to be produced here; whilst Dr. William Borlase stated in his *Natural History of Cornwall* that an earthquake shock was felt in the mine in 1757 at a depth of 20 fms. However, around the year 1772 the adventurers abandoned her, despite the phenomenal quality of her tin. Fifty years later that shrewd mining speculator James Halse, M.P. for St. Ives, decided to investigate the property. He consulted two knowledgeable old miners who had worked in Wheal Reeth in their younger days, and took down from them in his own hand statements concerning the mine and the reasons for its closing. These documents are extremely interesting, constituting as they do what are probably the only surviving reports by practical men on any mine in this area during the eighteenth century.

They run as follows:

"Alexander Rowe, of the parish of Gulval, miner, aged seventy-one, says that he worked in Wheal Reeth two years before it stopped.

During which he worked upon tut and wages, partly about the cross-cut going from Pirate Shaft to Jolly Dick's pitch; but before he got to the end the mine was stopped. That, previous thereto, he had worked upon tut, or wages, in clearing the bottoms, where the engine had worked, and during the whole extent of the bottoms, which gave him the opportunity of seeing the Carrack Lode, which held whole, down from the adit to the bottoms, except some small parts. That the quantity of tin during his time was so great in the mine as to employ almost all the stamps's within three miles thereof, and not less than thirty pair"—pair of mules is meant here; there were no carts in those days, and the tin stuff, copper ore and coal were carried in sacks on these animals' backs. "That there were five captains and sometimes six, and in general about 250 men in the mine. The west part below the engine was hardly worked at all. That there were great differences among the adventurers, and gross mismanagement in consequence thereof, and that if the ore had been gold instead of tin it would not pay as an adventure. That the engine would not go more than seven strokes per minute, and then with working half her time would draw all the water. All which he was ready to testify upon oath. As witness his hand, April 1 1822. Alex. Rowe."

"Jas. Richards, of Trevalgan, in St. Ives, miner, aged seventy years. That he worked in Wheal Reeth about a year before she stopped, that he well knew the pair of men who worked on the north lode called Dick Nicholls', being about 10 fathoms west of Christopher Edwards' house and about 13 fathoms below the adit. That the lode was 5 ft. big, all regular ore, and one hundred barrows thereof producing one ton of white tin. And that such was the state thereof at the time that the mine was stopped. That the engine would not work more than seven strokes per minute, and that it did not work more than two-thirds of the time. The box was a ten-inch. That the mine was not stopped for poverty, but owing to dissentions among the adventurers and bad management; and was intended to be put to work again. On which account some of the pumps and tools were left under water and never got up. All which he is ready to testify upon oath if required. These workmen also stated that to their own knowledge there were great quantities of tin ore thrown by the tut and wages men to stull, and which would be found in the mine. And that, also, the chief part of the water came from a case of ground about 10 fathoms below the adit which could easily be taken up by a cistern."[1]

Encouraged by these statements, Mr. Halse determined to reopen the mine; and an engine was put to work there again on the following midsummer day. When the mine was drained, it soon became clear that the old miners' assertions were accurate in every particular. Some of the old pitwork still remained in the shaft, the principal parts consisting mainly of brass, the ordinary pumps being of wood cramped with iron, cast-iron pumps (*i.e.,* pipes) not then having come into use. This brass, when sold, realised about sufficient to defray the cost of new iron pit-work. The mine was so quickly got into paying condition and turned out so rich that it proved unnecessary to make a call on the adventurers.

James Halse derived a large part of his substantial fortune from this mine, which he worked successfully for a number of years.

Before proceeding further with this narration of the mine's history, it should be mentioned that its name seems to have been indiscriminately "borrowed" by at least one of its neighbours when Wheal Reeth itself was idle. Thus, in May 1813 one-eighth part of "Wheal Reeth Great Bounds" and of "Little Wheal Reeth Bounds" was offered for sale. In 1818, following the bankruptcy of Mr. Oxnam, of Rosehill, in Madron, the sett of "all that very promising Tin Mine, called Wheal Reeth, near Rocky Downs, in the parish of Towednack," was put up for auction with all its materials. The lease was for 21 years, 13 of which remained unexpired, but the lord was willing to grant an extension.[2] From its given location—in Towednack rather than Lelant—this mine does not appear to be identical with the original Wheal Reeth, but was possibly the undertaking later known as Reeth Consols (*q.v.*) which lay to the west.

In May 1827 Messrs. Halse & Hichens, solicitors, St. Ives, advertised for an experienced mine agent for the (genuine) "Wheal Reeth extensive Tin Mine in the parish of Lelant."[3] James Halse died in 1838. In that same year Davies Gilbert's *Parochial History of Cornwall* stated that Wheal Reeth had proved more productive of tin than any other mine except Wheal Vor, and had been prosecuted to a depth unexampled till within recent times, even in mines of copper. Another authority (Henwood) noted that it then had one 36″, three 20″ and one 15″ engines, and employed 231 people.

According to George Treweeke, the well known St. Ives mine captain, Wheal Reeth closed again in 1842, its materials being transferred to Wheal Margaret when that mine was set to work. This closing appears to have taken place under similar circumstances to that of 1772. The mine was still highly productive, with unlimited paying ground in sight. The miners themselves could not understand the reason for the shut-down, but ascribed it to the fact that the manager, who was a very big man, could not descend the ladders to supervise underground operations. When the men were ordered to take up the tram roads from the levels, some of them wept with sorrow and regret at the pity of the thing, to leave behind such fine paying lodes which would be sealed up by water and ruin—as they thought—for ever. Even the captain was touched, and said if ever he had to do it again, it should not be so, but the adventurers had decided that the mine must be stopped, and it was too late now. Under his predecessor, who had died, everything had been most prosperous. The true reason for the closing was probably the expense of drawing tin stuff from so great a depth with ancient machinery; and as the richest part of the workings lay under the hamlet of Trink it must have been very costly to tram the stuff from such a distance. Apart from all this, a disagreement had arisen between the adventurers and lords regarding dues.[4]

Fortunately, the stoppage was only temporary, working being resumed two years later (in 1844) by a new company. In December, 4-

128ths shares in Wheal Reeth, "a highly improving and prosperous Mine," were offered for sale;[5] clearly it had not lost its old and excellent reputation. A meeting of the adventurers in November 1846 considered the advisability of erecting another engine. John Batten, of Penzance, was elected purser in the place of Mr. Bosustow, who had been killed by falling into an old mine working when on horseback. A rich tin lode was discovered in August 1847 valued at £100 per fathom. At the account passed in May 1851 a dividend of £600 was shared out; this would have amounted to £1,200 "but for the loss sustained by the failure of the late pursers." The enterprise was, however, in a highly prosperous condition, and if the prevailing tin prices held the dividends would revive.[6]

The August meeting in 1852 showed a profit of £776 14s. on the quarter, and a dividend of £3 per share was declared.[7] Five years later some spare mining materials were offered for sale by auction; these included an excellent 30″ cylinder steam pumping engine, 9′ stroke, equal, without boiler; a 15¼″ steam whim, 4′ stroke, with boiler and cage complete; and a four-horse whim, with 10′ cage and shaft tackle.[8] The pumping engine, however, found no purchaser, and was re-offered privately in September, being then described as "built by Harvey & Co., Hayle." Those interested could apply to Richard Pearce, Edward Hearle Rodd, or Samuel Higgs.[9]

As one of the deeper mines in the district, Wheal Reeth was an obvious candidate for the installation of a man engine; and one of these appliances was placed in the mine in 1861 by George Eustice, jun., of Hayle. A 30″ pumping engine was adapted for the purpose, the rod, which had a stroke of 9′, being attached directly to the beam; it had a speed of 5-6 strokes per minute.[10]

Lord Kinnaird's Commission of Enquiry into the mines of Great Britain brought to light a number of interesting facts about Wheal Reeth in 1864. It was then under the management of Capt. Stevens and had reached a depth of 220 fms. in granite. There were two shafts about 100 fms. apart, one going to the 190 fm. level, the other to the bottom. The workings were extended 130 fms. W. of Frederick's shaft at the 180 fm. level, and 170 fms. E. of Stevens' shaft. The levels generally were narrow, being only about 3′ wide, and it was recommended that they be driven wider. The temperature in the lower levels ranged from 75 deg. to 77 deg. F. In the engine shaft the ladders were good and divided off from the pumping rods as far as the 120 fm. level. Winding was effected by skips drawn by chains. The man-engine enabled miners to ride to the 150 fm. level; it was of the single-rod type. "I notice here as is to be noticed in nearly every mine the absence of anything approaching protection at the ends of shafts in the different levels. They are left quite open with nothing to prevent a man walking directly into them. In many cases the men have to walk directly in front of the shaft or on a single plank over it, which cannot but be attended with danger." The man-engine and steam whim boilers were both provided with feed gauge cocks. Forty men changed their clothes over the boiler. The two boilers of the pumping engine were connected; the safety valve was leaking, and thirty men changed over them. The safety valve was also leaking on the steam stamps boiler. The changing house measured 40′ x 10′ x 10′, and had a fire and tube inside. It was very dirty and devoid of ventilation. Only the tutwork men changed here, all the tributers changing over the boilers, as mentioned above. The dressing floors were mostly shedded. Clearly, safety and comfort for the men were hardly given prior consideration at Wheal Reeth in those days.

Spargo, in 1865, added a few footnotes to Kinnaird. He gave depth of adit as 30 fms. and depth below 220 fms. The pumping engine was a 40″, stamps engine 30″, and man-engine 30″. Dues were 1-18th, payable to W.B. Tyringham. The labour force consisted of 180 men, 30 women and 30 boys.

The mine was now incurring substantial losses, but at the April meeting in 1865 the agents tried to cheer the adventurers by telling them that its prospects had improved during the quarter, and if the opening ground continued to prove as productive as it had been for some time past they hoped to increase the returns of tin. Their recommendation that an Eastern shaft be sunk was agreed to, it being resolved to carry out the work with all despatch.[11] A good discovery was made in the cross-cut N. at the 190 fm. level in July 1866. The value of the tin lode was estimated at 4s. per barrow, but only 18″ of the lode had been intersected.[12]

Unhappily, the mine soon after ran into serious difficulties; and in November a circular was issued convening a special meeting of shareholders to decide its future. "Wheal Reeth is one of the most extensive mines throughout the Lelant district, and we believe the levels at various points extend upwards of half a mile in length," stated a contemporary report. "The water is drained by an excellent 40″ cylinder engine. There is also a well laid out steam stamps and two or three winding engines. That admirable invention, the man-engine, is also here at work. In the various operations connected with the development of this large mineral sett the most ample means have always been provided by the present company, and we should estimate their outlay at not less than £30,000. We believe Sir William Williams is the largest shareholder, and now, owing to relinquishments, holds something like half the mine. In such a deep and extensive concern as this, the water charges are necessarily heavy. Added to this, the present price of tin tells most seriously on the total returns during a quarter's working. The principal tutwork operations were suspended last Friday (being the setting day), and provided a suspension is determined on it will necessarily throw out of employment between 300 and 400 persons."[13]

The meeting decided that suspension was unavoidable; the 400 hands were discharged, and payment of wages, which had amounted to between £5-700 monthly, ceased.[14]

In 1869 that remarkable mining personality Thomas Treweeke made an unsuccessful attempt to form a company for re-working Wheal Reeth and Giew Consols. During the following years the mine's rich leavings were exploited, yielding tin worth many hundreds of pounds, but no further effort was made to open Wheal Reeth again until 1903-4, when Capt. Matthew Curnow was the prime mover, but this also proved abortive. However, in 1906 the sett was taken up by the Wheal Reeth Mining and Exploration Co., of Lelant, who commenced operations in February by cutting a trench N. and S. through the property, which disclosed three parallel E. and W. lodes varying in width from 12 to 20 inches. It was decided to sink a prospect shaft on each. One lode was thought to be a continuation of the Wheal Reeth or Mother lode. These operations were all in virgin ground, being a long way E. of any workings shown on the plans. Two of the lodes were quite new. It was hoped to work the old mine in conjunction with the new. The company consisted of local gentlemen, operations being in charge of Capt. T.F. Uren.[16]

The sett they had obtained ran from the northern slope of Trencrom Hill to the eastern side of Trink Hill, the principal centre of activity being about a thousand feet from the old workings. Further exploration revealed a fourth E. and W. lode; whilst in May three rich "seams"—*veins* was probably meant—of tin were found running through a strata of kaolin. They were 14, 6½ and 6 inches in width respectively, and produced very high assay values ranging from 300 to 57 lbs. of tin per ton.[17] Unfortunately, this promising start was not maintained; and by the beginning of 1909 only two men were being employed there, apparently on maintenance work. The company sank only two shallow shafts about 10 fms. deep on Durloe lode, but appears to have achieved little in the way of further development.

Dines gives the recorded output of Wheal Reeth as 1,955 tons of black tin between 1837-9 and 1853-67. These figures, however, do not cover the highly productive early phases of the mine's working.

Wheal Reeth appears to have been almost unique among the local mines in smelting its own tin. According to the late Mr. John Curnow, the old smelting house was situated near the former beershop known as The Wink at Cripple's Ease. As much as 100 tons of tin were refined here in a single month. These traditions are strikingly confirmed by actual records which show, however, that the smelter only operated for two years, producing 147 blocks of tin in 1823 and 1,024 in 1824.[18]

1. *St. Ives By The Sea* 1904
2. *Royal Cornwall Gazette* January 24 1818
3. *Royal Cornwall Gazette* May 5 1827
4. *St. Ives By The Sea* 1904
5. *Penzance Gazette* December 11 1844
6. *Cornish Telegraph* May 30 1851
7. *Cornish Telegraph* September 15 1852
8. *Cornish Telegraph* March 11 1857
9. *Cornish Telegraph* October 7 1857
10. Tew, D.H., *Man Engines in Cornwall* (Trevithick Society's *Journal,* No. 8, 1981)
11. *Cornish Telegraph* April 12 1865
12. *Cornish Telegraph* August 1 1866
13. *Cornish Telegraph* November 7 1866
14. *Cornish Telegraph* November 28 1866
15. *Cornish Telegraph* October 20 1869
16. *Western Echo* March 3 1906
17. *Western Echo* May 23 1906
18. Barton, D.B., *A History of Tin Mining and Smelting in Cornwall* 1967

EAST WHEAL REETH (NANCE MOOR)

In May 1813 and again in January 1815 there was advertised for sale one-third share of a pair of stream and mine bounds in Nance Moor, Lelant. Nance farm lies in the valley to the north of Trink Hill, and several small scale mining ventures were started here on the lodes which course in an E.-W. direction through the hill. One of these was inaugurated in 1850 under the name of East Wheal Reeth. In May 1852 it was reported to have a lode widening in the shaft, the latter then being five fathoms below the 24 fm. level.[1] On April 11 1854 the mine was divided into 6,000 shares, and a new code of rules adopted; at the same time a call of 1s. 6d. was imposed.[2] However, on July 17 the adventurers, considering it impossible to carry out any further development, resolved to abandon the enterprise and sell the materials, the proceeds to be used to meet the company's liabilities.[3]

1. *Cornish Telegraph* February 3 1852
2. *Cornish Telegraph* April 28 1854
3. *Cornish Telegraph* August 25 1854

WHEAL SARAH

In 1817 Wheal Sarah, at St. Ives, was said to have sold 73 tons of copper ore for £461; whilst in 1838 it employed 12 persons. This mine is believed to have been located in the vicinity of Wheal Kitty, of the Wheal Sisters group. There was also a Wheal Sarah in Crowan, and others of that name are known to have existed elsewhere in the county.

WHEAL SISTERS

Between the village of Nancledra, on the west, and the rounded, rock-strewn summit of Trencrom Hill, to the east, lies a stretch of pleasant rolling countryside, now devoted entirely to farming, but which, during the last century, was dominated by the smoking stacks, roaring stamps and busy tinyards of a series of important mines known by the collective name of Wheal Sisters. The principal members of this sorority were Wheals Mary, Kitty and Margaret; these formed a fairly tight complex at the centre of the group, Mary and Margaret lying to the west, and Kitty to the east adjacent to the hamlet of Polpeor. Flanking this trio were Old Tincroft Consols, just east of Nancledra, and Trencrom, lying under the western slope of Trencrom Hill. They all worked a group of lodes which coursed in a roughly E.N.E. direction for a distance of about a mile and a quarter between Nancledra and Trevarrack and a transverse distance of a quarter of a mile between Trink Hill and Trencrom.

An exhaustive description of the Wheal Sisters lode system and the development work carried out thereon has been given by Dines, only a brief summary of which need be inserted here. Wheal Mary lode is the northernmost of the series; it intersects Wheal Kitty Sump lode 420 yards E. by N. of Brunnion hamlet. Another lode lies to the N.E. of the eastern extremity of Wheal Mary lode. A hundred yards S. of Wheal Mary lode lies a lode known as North Russo on the west, Wheal Kitty Sump further east, and after the intersection South of it again runs a lode known as Bramble lode in Old Tincroft section, Wheal Margaret lode in Wheal Margaret section, and Mushell's lode in Wheal Kitty section. South Russo lode branches from the hangingwall of Mushell's lode, and divides into North and South Branches. Wicker's lode lies about midway between the eastern ends of the levels on Mushell's and South Russo lodes. Trencrom Mine worked a lode almost in alignment with Fox's lode in Wheal Kitty.

The various mines comprising Wheal Sisters each had histories as separate workings which are related under their individual names. The big amalgamation which led to the establishment of Wheal Sisters took place in 1875; but prior to this a number of short lived working arrangements seem to have been entered into between certain members of the group, which is not surprising, considering their close proximity to one another and the fact that at least three of them had interconnected drainage systems.

Dines gives records of copper and tin production from "Wheal Sisters" between 1825-48, and surmises that a small property may have borne that name before the amalgamation. The *Penzance Gazette* of March 10 1847 gives an abstract of this mine's acounts for November and December of the previous year, showing that £1,264 worth of copper had been sold and £835 paid in wages. There are also records relating to "Mary and Kitty United" (1860-2) and to "Mary and Trencrom" (1877.)

Some curious traditions concerning the three "sisters" were preserved in that invaluable compilation *St. Ives By The Sea* (1904.) "Wheal Mary was the oldest mine, and also the largest. Her workings ranged from the engine house at Plowress Hill to Wheal Cuckoo by Cripple's Ease. She had five large steam engines, two of which were for pumping and two for hoisting. All her tinstuff was stamped at the water stamps at Locke, in the valley south of Nancledra. Wheal Margaret, next in size, had two pumping engines, two hoisting engines, and a fire-stamps. She gave many thousands of pounds in dividends to the original adventurers. Kitty and Trencrom each possessed one pumping, one winding and one stamping engine. Margaret and Kitty were connected with the manor of Trembethow, which received more than £60,000 in dues from them. The Bolitho family had an interest in some of these mines, and purchased Wheal Margaret of Messrs. Lee and Treweeke. Mr. Field, of Marazion, was the principal representative of the adventurers in Trencrom, which was taken over at a valuation, and so these four mines were amalgamated by Messrs. Bolitho, Field & Co. under the appropriate name of Wheal Sisters. This event considerably clipped the wings of the miners, for previously when they were sacked from one mine they would look for a job at another, but now this chance was not allowed them, it was all one concern, and their independent days were at an end."

So much for tradition. The actual cause of the merging of the mines into a united enterprise was the exceptionally wet winter of 1874-5. In December the collapse of an adit in Wheal Margaret produced serious flooding there as well as in Kitty and Mary. By January 1875 the heavy rains were seriously threatening the existence of all three. The water in Wheal Mary was 130 fms. deep; and it was alleged that Wheals Margaret and Kitty (which had recently combined, under pressure from the lords, to ensure more economical working) had inadequate engine power to cope with the flood. The Wheal Mary adventurers, seeing little hope of saving the mine by their own efforts, gave notice to the lord (Mr. Praed) that they would abandon her if Margaret and Kitty (with 110 and 100 fms. of water respectively) would not contribute to the cost and effort required to dislodge the common foe.[1]

The unsisterly quarrel persisted for some time. By October, deep work in all the mines was suspended. The water had risen to the 70 fm. level in Mary and Margaret, which had four engines each, and to the 80 in Kitty, which had three engines. The livelihood of 500 workers was at risk; and what made the situation even more tragic was the fact that the mines were still far from exhausted—Wheal Mary, 220 fms. deep, had rich tin ground in her bottom. The two interests involved—Messrs Bolitho, on the one hand, and Mitchell & Co. of Marazion, on the other—argued the question profitlessly for several months. Mr. T.W. Field (for Mitchell & Co., and for Wheal Mary, of which he and his friends owned 5-6ths) maintained that Wheal Margaret and Polpeor (Wheal Kitty) in which Messrs. Bolitho and their associates held 5-6ths, should pay £500 compensation for the damage caused by allowing water to accumulate. Faced with the onset of another potentially disastrous winter, the two parties decided it would be mutually advantageous to forget their differences and solve the water question once and for all by amalgamating their mines.[2]

News of this settlement caused heartfelt rejoicing at Lelant. The following letter typifies the prevalent feeling at that time:

"Myself and many others are glad to hear that the three sisters, Mary, Margaret and Kitty, are now become reconciled, after a very long debate and much contention. And although there have been anything but sisterly feelings existing between them, it seems they are now brought into one family circle; and like sisters should be, to bear one another's burden. Had there continued discord, contention and divisions, it certainly would have been of great importance to this district, for it would have thrown many men and women out of employ, and what is still worse, into poverty and distress. But the miners' faces now seem to be lit up with new hopes of better days, and a better state of things. Like sisters, they may be a great blessing to those who have the charge over them. There is yet, I believe, hidden treasures in the hearts of these sisters, which will well repay the parental labour and sacrifice expended. In their past history, they have been, in no way, a burden, but a blessing for many years to the employed and employer. Granted that Margaret has gone astray of late, so as to become a despised and rejected sister, yet, I believe, there is hidden, deep in her heart, a treasure that will in no way disgrace the family with which she stands identified. Wishing those gentlemen success who so nobly fought for this much improved state of things, and hoping the sisters will be to them a great blessing, I remain, An Acquaintance of the Family."[3]

Although there was no mention of Trencrom joining the group, this mine became linked with the others at this time through its being controlled by Wheal Mary adventurers, who had been subsidising it from the profits of Wheal Mary.

In September 1876 it was announced that Wheal Sisters was looking much better throughout, and increased returns were anticipated against a diminished expenditure. Clearly, the beneficial results of the amalgamation were beginning to be felt at this time. Unhappily, the disastrous fall in tin prices which took place during the following year, together with the heavy cost of running three steam pumping engines, steam stamps and steam whims, robbed the adventurers of the benefits which should have accrued to them. So, in July 1877 the mine was reported to be running at a loss, though 30 tons of tin were being sent away monthly. However, had the merger not taken place, it seems unlikely that any of the constituent enterprises would have survived this difficult period which saw the closure of nearly every other mine in the district.

A fatal accident occurred at Trencrom in January 1878 when Richard Thomas of Lelant was crushed by a large stone he was attempting to take down in the 80 fm. level.[4] The falling price of tin soon afterwards began to hit the adventurers very hard. At the six months' account held in February 1879 an adverse balance of £1,037 was disclosed, requiring a £1 10s. call. Altogether, 271 tons 16 cwt. of tin had been sold, realising £8,992. Capt. Rosewarne reported that in Wheal Mary, Engine shaft was sunk to the 130 fm. level, the lode E. worth £5 per fm. and W. £3 per fm.

In the lift from the 120 to the 130 fm. level the lode had been disordered by the cross-course being in the shaft, but by its underlying W. it was now got to the western end, and the lode in the present bottom was looking much better. Hollow's Flat-rod shaft was sinking from the 150 to the 160 fm. level, set by contract to eleven men for £120; the lode in the shaft had opened tribute ground. The 150 and 140 levels E. and W. of Hollow's were all driving. The lode in the 180 E. of Fox's shaft had been followed through good tribute ground; and as the 170 level far in advance of this end also looked very promising, excellent returns were anticipated from the lower level. In the 180, 170, 160 and 150 fm. levels on Wheal Mary lode valuable results had lately been obtained, and they intended immediately opening on the lode at shallow levels, and for this purpose had set a cross-cut to drive at the 140, which already appeared to be nearing it. This was quite a distinct bunch of tin from that being worked about Wheal Mary Engine shaft, and when fully laid open should be equally profitable.

In Wheal Kitty, six men were driving a cross-cut N. of the North Gowan lode, to intersect North Russia (*sic*) lode, which would be cut in about four fms. further driving. In Wheal Margaret, the lode in the winze sinking below the adit was producing low quality tinstuff. It seems clear from this report that attention was being concentrated in the Trencrom and Mary sections, Kitty and Margaret being practically abandoned. Complaint was made that exceptionally wet weather had lessened the returns; but their prospects were never better. A total of 550 persons was employed in the mines. Mr. T.W. Field said he was sorry that success seemed to be running away from them as fast as it could. Three years ago their tin realised £47 a ton; if only they had that price today, instead of making a call, they would have declared a dividend.[5]

In April, the widows of two miners who had been killed in Wheal Sisters were each sent to prison for a fortnight with hard labour by Camborne magistrates for stealing 90 lbs. of coal belonging to the adventurers—this despite an appeal from Capt. Rosewarne, the manager, for leniency. Each left a family of children to be provided for whilst serving sentence.[6] Further evidence of the prevailing harsh living conditions was provided at the five-monthly account in October. Field then explained that the reduced output of 188 tons of tin and the consequent working loss of £634 was attributable to the scarcity of men, a large number of whom had left the mine to go potato digging. The fact that agricultural labourer's wages were found more attractive than those offered by the mine tells its own grim story. The adventurers were faring no better. When the mines had been amalgamated, the first parcel of tin sold had realised £47 10s. per ton, and they thought the price could not possibly go any lower. Nevertheless, it subsequently declined by 33%, and they had sold some tin at just over £30 a ton. During the last four years no less than £16 10s. per share had been called up, of which amount nearly £6,000 had been paid by Messrs. Bolitho, over £4,000 by himself and friends, and a further large sum by Messrs. Harvey & Co., Mr. Coulson, and others. Some adventurers had forfeited their shares; and of these, 100 would be sold at £15 each to help reduce the heavy debit balance of £3,539.

Field conceded they had always found the men ready and willing to support them in their endeavours to carry on the concern. "We told the men that if it was a question simply of consulting our own interests, the best thing would be to close the mine, because we saw little or no prospect of the mines paying, and we were really and truly carrying on the concern for the benefit of the district, and nothing else. The men saw this, and cheerfully submitted to the reduction of wages which had been found necessary from time to time. But it is now my very great pleasure to be able to tell them that on the coming Saturday their standard will be increased from £35 to £40 a ton, and I hope the tin market will go on still further improving, so that before long we might again be able to add to the men's wages." The price of tin had, in fact, risen by the unprecedented amount of £26 a ton in the past ten weeks, so one wonders why the men could not have been given a little more.

Capt. Rosewarne explained that some of their financial difficulties had been the direct result of the amalgamation. It had been determined not to work the mines on a hand-to-mouth basis, but for a permanency, which involved a great deal of "dead work," the benefits of which, however, would soon be felt. The sett was very extensive, and contained many productive lodes. They had no rich bunches in width, but some lodes contained a long line of productive tin ground. He expressed disappointment that the bottom levels of Wheal Mary had not turned out better of late, but did not despair, as it was a characteristic of these mines that when they had one rich level the next one was invariably not so good. At the present time they were going through a hard bar of ground, but having passed it would be able to raise a large quantity of stuff. Attention was now being directed to bringing back the water from Wheal Kitty and the whole of the eastern mines, from the 110 fms. level, to Trencrom engine which up to that time had had comparatively little to do. It had been necessary to keep the pumping engine at work at Giesler's, but before another winter came on they would have holed the ground from Trencrom right through to Wheal Kitty, and could then dispense with that engine and develop all the South lode 110 fms. from surface, dry. Giesler's lode had recently been inspected by a mining expert, who described it as a large lode, principally containing caple, which should prove valuable in depth. Little had been done at Ambrose's shaft, owing to the low price of tin, attention being concentrated instead on Hollow's Flat-rod, where the lode seemed to be increasingly productive and lengthening back towards Engine shaft. The 60 and 70 fm. levels W. of Ambrose's had been cleared; it was hoped to clear more of the shallower levels in the next few months and find a large quantity of payable tin ground. In Margaret, little tutwork had been done for some time, but the Standard lode had been driven on in the 140, where it was hoped soon to find something valuable.[7]

At the June account in 1880 a small loss of £361 was disclosed; 142 tons of tin had been sold, but the average price received was only £49 10s., compared with £52 10s. in the previous 16 weeks. Capt. Rosewarne reported very good progress in sinking Wheal Mary Engine shaft. The bottoms of Wheal Mary and Trencrom were opening out very satisfactorily. The ends of Wheal Margaret had improved, and they had good expectations of cutting something good by continuing the 200 and 210 fm. level crosscuts S. Over 500 persons were employed in the mine.

"Captain Nemo" of the *Cornish Telegraph* reported at this time that Capt. Rosewarne, of Wheal Sisters, and mineral agent to the Rev. H.M. St. Aubyn, was a candidate for the coveted post of H.M. Inspector of Mines for the Western District. "The position is one which should be filled by a man possessing sound practical mining knowledge, as well as having an intimate acquaintance with the county. In these respects, Capt. Rosewarne is in every way qualified for the office." However, despite having the support of the mining interests of West Cornwall, Capt. Rosewarne did not obtain the appointment.

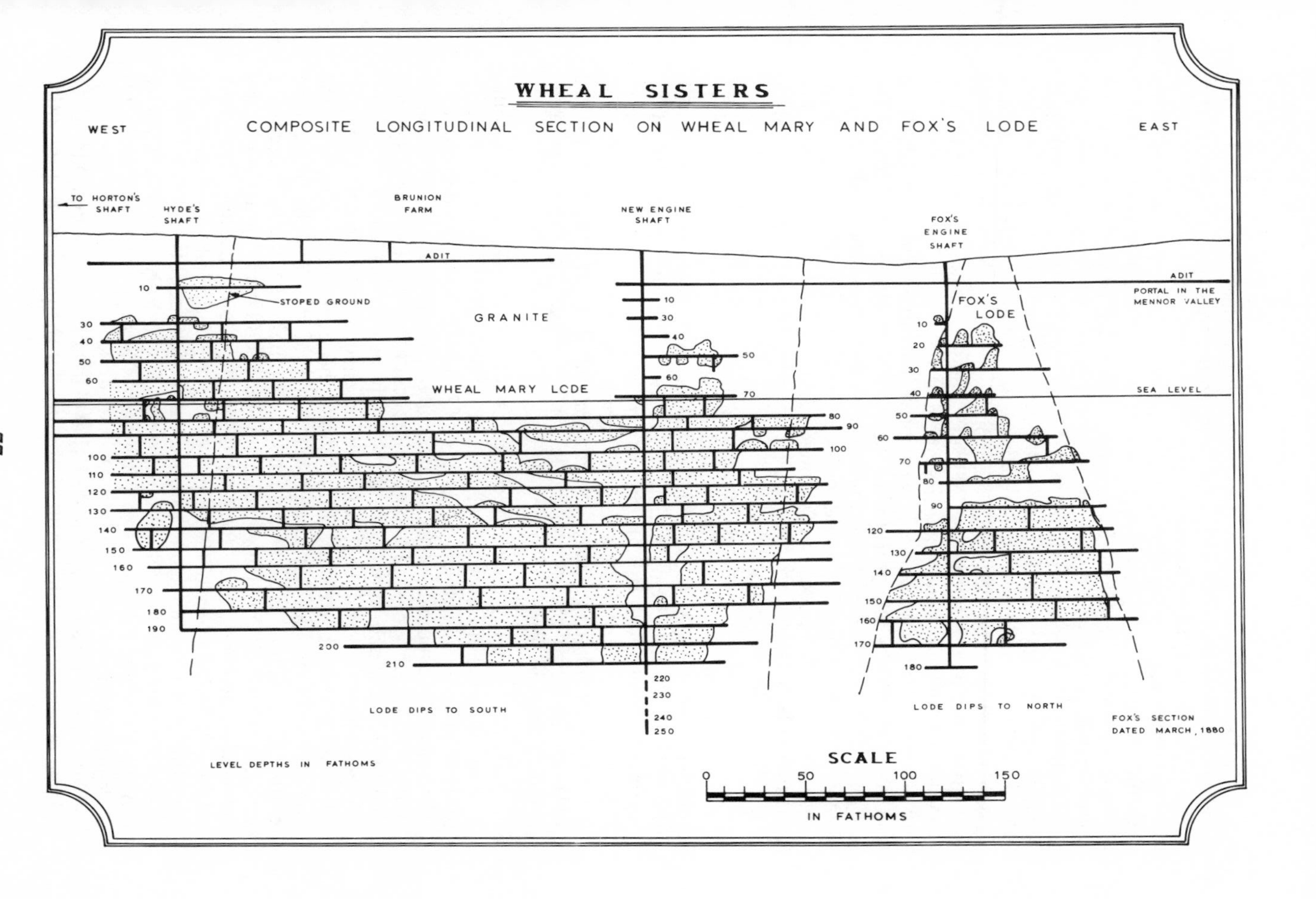
WHEAL SISTERS
COMPOSITE LONGITUDINAL SECTION ON WHEAL MARY AND FOX'S LODE
WEST
EAST
TO HORTON'S SHAFT
HYDE'S SHAFT
BRUNION FARM
ADIT
STOPED GROUND
GRANITE
WHEAL MARY LODE
NEW ENGINE SHAFT
FOX'S ENGINE SHAFT
FOX'S LODE
ADIT
PORTAL IN THE MENNOR VALLEY
SEA LEVEL
FOX'S SECTION DATED MARCH, 1880
LODE DIPS TO NORTH
LODE DIPS TO SOUTH
LEVEL DEPTHS IN FATHOMS
SCALE
IN FATHOMS
0
50
100
150

In February 1881 one of the principal shareholders disposed of his interest, which had the effect of further depressing the value of the shares. However, the discovery of a lode worth about £30 per fathom had since brought them into better demand. A loss of £1,407 had been sustained during the quarter (sixteen weeks), and a call of 5s. per 6,000th share was imposed. Capt. Rosewarne reported that the severe weather had caused a loss of 12 tons on their tin sales; this was presumably a reference to the great blizzard of that year, which caused such widespread damage and distress. Although output from Wheal Mary had fallen off, production from Trencrom was steadily increasing. It was soon hoped to intersect the lodes south of Wheal Mary shaft in the Polpeor part of the sett at the 200 fm. level—lodes which, at shallower levels, had yielded large quantities of tin.[8]

William John Williams, a twenty-two year old miner, met his death in February 1882 while putting in a ladder sollar between the 180 and 190 levels. He had ascended a short distance to fetch some tools, and coming down the ladder burdened with hammer, poker, borer and pick, missed his footing and fell about ten fathoms, sustaining fatal head injuries. The printed rules required that all equipment of this kind should be sent in the kibble, and not carried.[9]

At the 16 weeks' account in June, presided over by T.W. Field, the purser, 101 tons of tin were shown to have realised £5,496, the loss on the quarter being £1,253. A call made at last account had produced £1,439, the adverse balance being £1,367, to reduce which a further call of 5s. was made. Faced with this gloomy situation, a proposal was made to sell the mine and rework it as a limited liability concern. A special meeting was called in July to consider this matter; but it appears that an upward turn in the price of tin was largely responsible for the adventurers deciding to carry on.

Affairs certainly looked more promising at the 20 weeks' account held on the mine in October. 153 tons of tin had been sold for £8,814, the average price being £60 2s. per ton, or £2 more than at the last account. The loss on five months' working amounted to only £51, so that the mine was about meeting cost. The agents reported that since the last meeting the mine had much improved, particularly in the bottom levels. About 440 persons were employed. A discussion ensued as to the desirability of purchasing rock boring machinery, but the question was left for the committee to decide. Mr. Peter Watson said it would be some time before they could expect dividends, although the mines were in a satisfactory condition. They had lots of lodes and many shafts sunk, and splendid machinery and dressing floors laid out. If, however, they ultimately found more drawing power was needed, that would be a very easy matter when they came to open out a rich lode. It was resolved to subscribe two guineas per annum to the Royal Polytechnic Society so that prizes might be offered to youngsters for suggesting improvements in regard to mining.

In March 1883 it was stated that Mr. Praed, through Mr. R.C. Glanville, his agent, had remitted all dues for the previous four months, amounting to £120, in consideration of the increase of water charges and other difficulties. One forty-eighth of the dues were previously charged, and the mine had uniformly been treated in the most liberal way by the lord.

By December prospects had so much improved that Messrs. Harvey, of Hayle, and Mitchell, Field & Co., of Trereife, purchased all the available (230) shares. Wheal Mary Engine shaft was then 240 fms. deep; and 40 fms. from it, in the 230 level, a winze sunk seven fathoms had proved the tin lode already seen in the shaft to be much richer there. Some of the ore was "splendid," containing quite 50% of pure tin, whilst the lode had gone down into decomposed granite with many veins of tin disseminated through it. As this soft ground extended from the winze to the shaft it was hoped that about three months' work might show a new feature in Wheal Mary and lead to a change in the fortunes of Wheal Sisters, on whom a thousand persons depended directly or indirectly for their livelihood.[10]

Two remarkable events were recorded in 1886. The first occurred in April when, during a severe thunderstorm, a large stack was struck by lightning and demolished, some heavy stones being found over 100 yards away. An electric shock was felt by two miners working in the 200 fm. level, one receiving a blow as if struck on the back by a hilt.[11] The second incident took place on May 7, which was described as a red-letter day in the history of the mine. It appears that for some time previously Capt. Rosewarne had experienced difficulty in persuading carriers to convey coal to Wheal Sisters, these men preferring to work their own land. Fearing the engines would soon become idle he engaged Messrs. Trewhella, of St. Erth, to bring in eleven tons of coal with their traction engine. At around five o'clock on the appointed day the inhabitants for miles around assembled at Wheal Kitty to witness its arrival. The coal was taken on at Hayle, and the engine ran so successfully over the narrow roads and in and out of the coal yards as to assure Capt. Rosewarne that he need no longer consider horses as his onlv resource.

Offsetting this good news, however, a persistent rumour circulated concerning the impending closing of the mine, "and when news comes out that the mines are to go on as before the men seem to look upon it as an interposition of Providence in their behalf." Hopeful signs were not altogether wanting. There had been an improvement at Hollow's, while the 240 and 250 ends and stopes at Wheal Mary, especially the ground E. of Wheal Mary shaft, had lately been more productive than in any former period of the mine's history. Capt. Rosewarne was handicapped in developing these possibilities by being compelled to work on a restricted scale. "The mines in this neighbourhood have yielded immense dividends. The price list of tin stuff raised at Wheal Reeth before the winding-up of that mine is positive evidence of the richness of that lode extending eastward. This ground, with all the run east of Wheal Mary, has never been developed. A prospect of this kind existing in the larger mining districts of Camborne or Redruth would have been considered worthy of a bold and vigorous method of operation, and would doubtless finally reward any spirited company of adventurers."[12]

In February 1887 Capt. W. Rosewarne discovered a new lode at grass in the Brunnion-field, which promised to be of good value. A quantity of stuff taken from 4 fms. depth assayed 96 lbs. of tin to the ton, the test being witnessed by many visitors drawn to the mine by news of the rich discovery. The field had been last worked in 1832, and William Glasson, of Lelant, drove the horse whim there until it was abandoned. "It was not altogether unproductive at that time, and Capt. Williams remembers stamping many tons of tin raised here." The importance of the lode was underlined by the fact that it lay parallel to another in an adjoining field from which James Halse acquired his wealth.[13]

The quarterly meeting held later that month showed a loss of £756, resulting in a call of 5s. per 3625th share. The exploratory end of the 250 fm. level W. of Wheal Mary Engine shaft had been driven to within six fathoms of the new lode, of which great things were expected. The eastern end of this level was nearing the cross-course, east of which, in the 240, there had been an excellent lode. In the latter level they had recently intersected what was believed to be Wheal Kitty lode, where it was expected to lay open valuable tin ground. In Trencrom mine, Hollow's Flat-rod shaft had been set to sink 11 fms. below the 210, the lode being worth for the length of the shaft (12′) £12 per fm. The 210 fm. level was driving both E. and W., the western ground being unusually hard. The 200 E. and W., 190 W., 180 E. and 40 W. were all driving. At Fox's shaft, the 220 E. had greatly improved since passing through the cross-course. The lode in the 70 E. of Giesler's Engine shaft, on South Russoe lode, in Wheal Kitty, was worth £4 per fm., and £5 in the 60 E. Within the last fortnight work had begun clearing a shaft near Brunnion farm house, formerly called Wheal Pink, which had ceased working 55 years before. At a depth of 6½ fms. the lode was 4' wide, in easy ground. Judging from what was being removed from the shaft it must have been a very good lode, the refuse producing 15 lbs. of tin per ton of stuff.[14]

The January 1888 meeting was held at the Chyandour offices of Messrs Bolitho, the largest shareholders, whose share of the 8s. call amounted to £845, making £2,500 paid by them in the past twelve months. Later that year (September) a singular fatal accident took place. Two tributers, Curnow and Ninnis, were working in the 40 fm. level at Harding's shaft—a place known to be dangerous, and where they would have been subject to a fine if discovered. While getting off a piece of lode from the flat wall, Ninnis driving in a wedge to split it off, a mass of rubbish came down and buried them both. Ninnis managed to free himself, but Curnow was killed. At the inquest, Curnow said that he and his comrade knew of no rule against "scramblers" working where they liked; but Capt. Rosewarne proved that the rule existed, and was strictly enforced.[15]

Meanwhile, apprehensions concerning the future of Wheal Sisters continued to grow. A correspondent signing himself "S.K." wrote that "it is touching to hear the miners remark as they meet in the dry in the mornings that next Saturday is likely to seal the fate of the mine. . . The day that saw (it) closed would be a dark and gloomy one, a day that would live long in the memories of the miners and their children." Wheal Sisters had been paying £12,000 a year in wages and £6-7,000 in merchants' bills, whilst tin sales had been running at 60-70 tons every four months. Closure at this time would be all the more lamentable since the 210 (the bottom) end at Fox's was richer than ever, producing no less than 240 lbs. of tin to the ton of stuff! whilst the last three tons of stuff sent up from Hollow's shaft yielded 80 lbs. to the ton.

However, in spite of these favourable omens, the financial position continued to deteriorate. During a meeting held at Chyandour on September 5, with Mr. T. Bedford Bolitho, M.P., presiding, a loss of about £1,800 was disclosed on 16 weeks' working, the total debit balance being £2,290. Although Capt. Rosewarne optimistically reported improvements at several points of the mine, the adventurers, smarting under the sting of a 12s. 6d. call, adjourned the meeting to the 8th in order to get an independent opinion. "Wheal Sisters, which is the only mine working in the Lelant district, has been working at a loss for several years past. The shares are held by less than half-a-dozen shareholders, of whom the principal are the Messrs. Bolitho. The mine has only been kept

Repairing a damaged engine house at Wheal Sisters after it had been struck by lightning in April 1886. (R.I.C.)

on for the sake of the hundreds of men who would be thrown out of employment if the operations were suspended. It is, however, probable that unless a more hopeful report be given by an outside agent, the mine will be stopped at once." The outside agent chosen to inspect the property was Capt. Bishop, of East Pool; and his assessment, when presented at the adjourned meeting, proved so encouraging that the adventurers resolved to withdraw the notice they had previously given to the lords of their intention to abandon the mine, and instead carry out Capt. Bishop's recommendations, which were to open out and thoroughly develop it.

Unfortunately, in May 1889, whilst this work was in progress, certain trustees who held a considerable interest in Wheal Sisters were obliged to wind up the trust estates and sever their connection with it. The other shareholders, finding themselves unable to carry on, resolved to sell the mine as a going concern, hoping that a limited liability company might be formed to take it over. Messrs. Bolitho and Sons, and others, who held a majority of shares in the old company undertook to apply for a large holding in the new one.

The prospectus of the Wheal Sisters Mining Company, Limited, was issued in May 1890; the capital would consist of 25,000 £1 shares. The property was held under setts, at 1-18th and 1-24th dues; but no dues had been paid for some time past, and the lords had consented to forego them until dividends were declared, with the offer of a renewal for 21 years at 1-24th dues on expiry. The machinery comprised a 60″ pumping engine, 10′ stroke in cylinder and 9′ in shaft, with four boilers of 11 tons each; a 40″ do., 10′ stroke in cylinder, 9′ in shaft, with two 11 tons boilers; a 28″ do., 6′ stroke, equal beam, with 8½ tons boiler; a 36″ pumping and stamping engine with 11 tons boiler and 32 heads of stamps; a 26″ pumping engine, 8′ stroke, equal beam, with 9 tons boiler; a 30″ stamping engine, with 32 heads of stamps; two 24″ winding engines, each with a 7 tons boiler; a 24″ stamping engine, with 10 tons boiler and 20 heads of stamps; and a 20″ whim engine with 10 tons boiler. There was also a 20″ cylinder air compressor, recently erected at a cost of over £600, and a large quantity of materials and tools of all descriptions.

The lack of success of the old company was attributed to insufficient capital for the proper development of such a large undertaking. As a result, the reserves had been taken away faster than the ground was laid open, receipts ceased to meet expenditure, and calls became frequent. Despite this, £250,000 worth of tin had been sold since the 1875 amalgamation, whilst previously £200,000 in profits were paid from the individual mines. At the present time about 18 tons of tin per month were being produced, but the mine had sufficient machinery for returning 50 tons. It was proposed to concentrate the pumping and dressing plant, to reduce working costs. The shallower levels had yielded large returns, from 30-50 tons of tin per month; Trencrom shaft would accordingly be sunk to intersect these lodes at greater depth. Several known, but unwrought, lodes which traversed the sett would be opened up, and good

Wheal Sisters

The engine house on the right is the same as that shown in the previous photo (No. 21). It appears to have been taken soon after the repairs were completed, the whitish patches on the roofs corresponding to the damaged areas in No. 21.

results were expected from them. The new promoters had bought out the old company for £4,500 in cash and £1,500 fully paid shares, leaving a balance of £19,000 to be subscribed; but it was anticipated only about £10-12,000 would have to be called up.

Capt. Josiah Thomas, manager of Dolcoath, in a report on the mine, stated that in recent years the workings had been principally on Wheal Mary and Trencrom lodes. Trencrom was the best part, but it had till recently been worked under great disadvantages. Engine shaft was only sunk to the 150 fms. level, whilst Hollow's, about 60 fms. further east, was sunk by the aid of underground flat-rods to the 220 fms. level, the various levels under the 150 being driven back under Engine shaft. The flat-rods frequently got out of order, causing some of the lower workings at Hollow's to be flooded and preventing the raising of tin. Quite recently, Engine shaft had been deepened from the 150 to the 210 fm. level and the 220 level driven west from Hollow's to meet it. For its entire length of 60 fms. it had followed a productive lode, worked on tribute from 8s. to 10s. in the £. When Engine shaft was sunk to the 230 and holed from the 210 to the 220, a great deal of valuable ground would be opened up.

Wheal Mary Engine shaft was sunk to the 250 fm. level, where there was good tribute ground; and from such a depth cross-cuts could be driven to intersect other lodes standing north and south. North Russoe lode was formerly very productive down to the 180 level, when they were compelled to abandon it for want of a shaft to draw the tin to surface. This lode could be intersected by a cross-cut at the 200 S. of Wheal Mary shaft in 70 fms. driving, and the same cross-cut continued 80 fms. further S. would meet Giesler's lode, which had only been worked down to the 70 fm. level, at which depth it was large and promising. Other lodes lay between it and Wheal Reeth, to the north, which could also be intersected by cross-cuts from Wheal Mary and Trencrom.

Capt. Thomas recommended driving a deep level from Trencrom to Wheal Mary, thereby enabling the pumping engine to be stopped, with a considerable saving in coal.

In a parallel report, Capt. Charles F. Bishop, of East Pool Mine, advised putting out cross-cuts south of Wheal Mary at about the 200 fm. level to reach the lodes which lay in that direction. Work on these had been stopped some time ago for want of proper communication with the winding shafts, but they were the most profitable in the sett, and had only been abandoned for want of sufficient capital to develop them. When inspecting the mine six months previously, he had found the water being kept out of Hollow's shaft (220 fms. deep) by flat-rods from Trencrom (150 fms.), and recommended rising from the 210 by boring machinery with all speed, and discontinuing the flat-rods at Hollow's. This work was now finished at the 210 except for putting in timbering from the 150 down to the 210. To reduce pumping charges, he advised putting back the 220 fm. level to unwater Fox's and Wheal Mary sections; this could be accomplished in about a year with boring machines, and would alsc open up valuable new tin ground. The productive lode in the 220 under Trencrom shaft was going to the north of Fox's in whole ground. If this were done, all the water could be raised by Trencrom engine. A stamps should be put in between Fox's and Trencrom capable of handling all the stuff on the mine; this would effect considerable economies.[16]

Unfortunately, the public subscribed only £9,000 out of the £25,000 required to reconstruct the mines, and the directors decided not to go to allotment. Wheal Sisters was thereupon closed, and all the hands discharged, this being a serious blow to employment in the neighbourhood. During the "electric pump" mining boom of 1906, however, it was announced that the sett, to which was added that of Lelant Consols, lying to the south, would be reworked by a new company. Operations began in March of the following year. The directors found it necessary to scotch a rumour that Chinese and Italian labour would be employed. "The first part of the programme will be an invitation to Cornish miners to work in the mines. If cottages cannot be had, the new company will erect them without the slightest hesitation. . . They do not anticipate any difficulty in getting good Cornish labour, but if there should be a shortage they will go outside the county."

In April, permission was granted to the Wheal Sisters Mining Company to lay a tramway crossing at Trencrom and Brunnion. By June, Wheal Mary Engine shaft had been enlarged from surface to bottom (250 fms.), whilst at Wheal Kitty a shallow adit was being cleared 600 yards to Polpeor. At Trencrom, where "some generations ago" the top of the old Sump shaft had fallen away, carrying with it a large portion of the engine house and causing a chokage 20 fms. from surface, a steam crane had been installed to clear the shaft. Fox's shaft, sunk to the 180, was being retimbered. Cottages were erecting, and a site being laid out for an electric power station. Trencrom had a steam sawmill driven by a portable engine which also supplied power to the steam crane. The Wheal Sisters group was drained by a three mile long adit, extending from Nancledra Valley through Wheal Margaret and the other sections to its second portal at Trevarrack; the Trevarrack end had been cleared to Trencrom. The mine had a new traction engine, and a tramroad was being laid from Trencrom to Wheal Mary shaft. An old miner was quoted to the effect that the two E.-W. lodes in Trencrom grew richer as they went deeper, but that the reverse was true of the four Wheal Mary lodes. At Wheal Margaret the principal lode was Cairnmore, reputedly highly prospective. Wheal Kitty had four lodes, including Cairnmore from Margaret. In the old days there were 32 heads of stamps at Wheal Kitty and Trencrom and 16 at Margaret. Among those who knew the district well, there was a tendency to pin their faith to Wheal Margaret.[17]

For about another year preparatory work went on apace; but then suddenly, in May 1908, it was announced that thirty of the employees had been discharged and others transferred to Wheal Merth, which was under the same management. The short-lived "boom" had collapsed, despite the fact that tin was still fetching £80 per ton—"a price beyond the dreams of those who, with slow, cumbersome and antiquated appliances, made the mine yield good dividends in the old days."[18] Wheal Sisters received its *coup de grace* in January 1909, and was never again reopened. Its most striking memorial, apart from the surviving engine houses, is the tower of Carbis Bay parish church, which was heightened in 1959 with granite blocks removed from the old power house at Trencrom.

Official records of production are, 1825-48 (Phillips and Darlington) 3,006 tons of copper ore sold for £16,257; 1877 (October) to 1900, 5,065 tons of tin ore sold for £239,610.

1. *Cornish Telegraph* January 20 1875
2. *Cornish Telegraph* October 13 1875
3. *Cornish Telegraph* February 9 1876
4. *Cornish Telegraph* January 8 1878
5. *Cornishman* February 20 1879
6. *Cornish Telegraph* April 8 1879
7. *Cornish Telegraph* October 29 1879
8. *Cornish Telegraph* February 17 1881
9. *Cornish Telegraph* February 16 1882
10. *Cornishman* December 6 1883
11. *Cornish Telegraph* April 8 1886
12. *Cornish Telegraph* May 13 1886
14. *Cornishman* February 17 1887
15. *Cornishman* January 26 and September 27 1888
16. *St. Ives Weekly Summary* May 31 1890
17. *St. Ives Weekly Summary* March 9 1907; *Western Echo* June 8 1907
18. *St. Ives Weekly Summary* May 30 1908 (quoting *Western Daily Mercury*)

WHEAL SPEED

Wheal Speed formed one of the constituents of the Providence Mines. It appears to have had at least two periods of independent existence, the first prior to the amalgamation of 1815 which resulted in the formation of the "United Mines of Wheal Comfort, Wheal Speed, Wheal Hazard, and East and West Wheal Crack;" and the second at some time before the establishment of the Providence Mines in 1832. The sale of 1-31st share in Wheal Speed tin and copper mine, in Lelant, was advertised to take place at the house of William Murley, in that parish, on September 27 1826.[1] In March of the following year a prematurely exploding charge caused the death of a miner named Hampton and the serious injury of another.[2] Wheal Speed sold 4,096 tons of copper ore for £23,306 between 1825 and 1843. As the mine, as far as is known, was a part of the Providence Mines from 1832, it is difficult to explain why these figures were separately recorded.

The fine engine house on Higgs' shaft (named after Samuel Higgs, purser of Providence Mines throughout nearly the whole course of their working) formed a prominent local landmark until its wanton destruction in 1967 during the construction of a housing estate.

On the slope of the hill behind this mine lay Little Wheal Speed, the old count house of which was the residence of the late Capt. Bruce Bainsmith, who contributed an interesting account of it to the *Old*

Cornwall journal in 1960. Adjoining this house is a sunken garden known as the Fuggan Pit, which was originally a blowing house where tin from the mine was smelted by charcoal. After the mine closed the pit was used for open-air religious services, like the more famous one a Gwennap; both Wesley and Billy Bray are reputed to have preached there. It was also pressed into service on a number of occasions for the less reputable entertainment of cock-fighting, a look-out being posted to give warning of the approach of any minions of the law. Whenever this happened the fighting-cocks were spirited away into the surrounding thickets, hymn books hastily produced, and the whole "congregation" broke into song. Some idea of the age of the mine was given by a brick found in the brick floor of the count house which bore the date 1634.

1. *Royal Cornwall Gazette* September 16 1826
2. *Royal Cornwall Gazette* March 17 1827

WHEAL STRAWBERRY

This sett lies just downstream of Trevethoe Mine in the steep-sided little valley which runs west from the Hayle-Penzance road near Canon's Town. The lode from which its name derives was worked from Strawberry shaft, and had a strike of about E. 25 degs. N.; Dines mentions further old shafts 150 yards south east of Splattenridden which may have been on this lode.

A singular fatal accident was reported from Wheal Strawberry in 1836. As a large number of men were lowering a lift of pumps, which was attached both to the capstan and cathead, the rope at the cathead gave way, throwing the whole weight on the capstan. This machine at once began to run at terrific speed, and carried everything before it into the shaft. The miners who stood on the capstan arms were hurled with great force in various directions, two being killed, a third fatally injured, and several others badly hurt. It appears the machine had been badly overloaded by sending down too many pumps at one time.[1]

In October 1905 it was said that the Trevethoe Mining Co., who were then working the nearby Wheal Merth, intended to place an engine on Wheal Strawberry shaft, and begin development there.[2] After the Trevethoe Co.'s interests were acquired by the Cornish Consolidated Tin Mines, Ltd., in 1906, Wheal Strawberry shaft was forked to the 10 fm. level, but being found full of debris was abandoned.[3]

1. *Royal Cornwall Gazette* May 6 1836. It is just possible that this accident occurred at Leedstown Wheal Strawberry, as the report did not locate the mine.
2. *St. Ives Weekly Summary* October 14 1905
3. *Western Echo* June 8 1907

WHEAL TRELOWETH

This mine lay at the head of Hayle Estuary, the sett embracing the area around St. Erth Railway Station. The lode, coursing E. 30 deg. N. and underlying 30 deg. N.W. on the W. side of Hayle River, was thought (according to Dines) to be an extension of the lode of West Wheal Alfred in the Gwinear district. In August 1820 12-61st parts in "Wheal Treloweth Copper Mine, lying and being in the several Parishes of St. Erth and Uny Lelant" were offered for sale; some very promising lodes had been recently discovered in it. The lodes then being worked in the adjoining Wheal Trelissick copper mine dipped into Treloweth, and the prospects were very encouraging. With the assistance of a steam engine, a very profitable adventure could be expected. The purser was Mr. Robert Bennett, of Camborne.[1] The materials of the mine were put up for auction on March 4 1822. These comprised a water wheel 32′ in diameter and 3′ on the breast; two whims, 9′ cage, with large iron pulleys, iron kibbles, etc.; and the usual assortment of pumps, ropes, dressing equipment and tools.[2]

1. *Royal Cornwall Gazette* August 26 1820
2. *Royal Cornwall Gazette* February 22 1822

TREMBETHOW

According to Dines, this mine was located 100 yards N.E. of Lock Farm, near Nancledra, and formed a part of Lelant Consols (*q.v.*) In the first quarter of 1825 885 bushels of tinstuff from Trembethow were stamped, and produced 8 tons 10 cwts. 1 qr. 1 lb. of black tin which, selling at prices between £42 and £45 per ton, realised £469 1s. 5d. After deducting expenses, the net amount of £227 14s. 9d. was divided between F.H. Rodd, Rev. H.H. Tremayne and Samuel Stephens (one-ninth each), exors. A. Champernowne (one quarter), and William Praed (one third).[1]

1. MS. Account 30th July 1825, *penes* Justin Brooke (1966)

TRENCROM

Near the road junction below Trencrom Farm a fine ivy-clad engine house marks the site of Trencrom mine, which lies on the extreme East of the Wheal Sisters sett. In 1860 it was making regular monthly returns of tin and hoped soon to be in a paying state; the shares, quoted at around £7 per 1,024th, were described as an excellent speculation.[1] Trencrom failed to emulate the success of her western neighbours, however, and the records for the next few years show a succession of debit balances and calls. At the quarterly meeting in July 1862 the loss amounted to £516, though tin sales had realised £1,484. The agents—Thomas Richards, Richard Hollow and Francis Bennetts—reported Engine shaft sunk 7 fms. below the 100; about 2 fms. above the shaft bottom the cross-course underlay West into the shaft, promising a better lode for tin; at present the lode was 2′ wide, worth £10 per fm., sinking for £16. The 16 aditional stamp heads were working very well, and sales of tin would gradually increase. Considering the general prospects of the shafts and levels, the mine had improved. 30 men were employed on tutwork and 42 on tribute.[2] By 1865 the workings had reached a depth of 110 fms. below adit (27 fms.)

Unfortunately, in April 1867, due to the low price of tin, Trencrom was "knocked," the materials being offered for sale by private contract. These included a 30″ cylinder 9′ stroke Bull pumping engine, with two boilers, about 20 tons; a 24″ cylinder 8′ stroke horizontal double winding engine, with cage, fly wheel, and 10 tons boiler; a 24″ cylinder 9′ and 8′ stroke single stamping and winding engine, with cage, fly wheel and 10 tons boiler; steam stamps, comprising two axles of 16 heads each (5 lifts to round) with the frames, heads, lifters, tongues, iron bottoms, guides and woodwork. All items were in good working order, and would be sold "a bargain."[3]

Despite its suspension, miners continued to regard Trencrom as one of the best prospects in the district; and in 1870, when the metal had risen in price again, a new company was formed to take up the sett, which was said to comprise a fine field for vigorous exploration.[4] Messrs. G. Eustice & Son, the well known mining engineers of Hayle, were reported in November 1871 to be erecting three engines at Trencrom—a 60″ for pumping, a 30″ for stamping and a 20″ for winding.[5]

The new proprietors of Trencrom also owned Wheal Mary, which was then making excellent profits, and these they now poured into the less prosperous mine, believing that "Trencrom may be looking up any day, and is very likely to do so in the good time that's coming, boys, if we wait a little longer."[6] A year later an unusual accident occurred at the mine. A suit of clothes seen hanging in the "dry" led to the suspicion that a miner named Thomas Hicks had met with a mishap underground. A search party went down Dawe's shaft and examined the 60 fm. level and pitch where he had been working. Their shouts at first met with no reply; but in answer to a second call they heard him cry "Come, clear me!" They found him in a back, completely covered, save for his face, by a quantity of stuff which had fallen away. He was extricated, but died soon after reaching surface. He had been working quite alone, a most unusual circumstance. His "take" had ceased on the previous Saturday and had not been renewed at the survey; it was thought he had been searching about in the old workings, to see if anything had been left.[7] During the following April another miner named Edward Uren, of Lelant Downs, lost his life when filling the skip at the 40 fm. level. The fatality occurred by his foot slipping as he crossed a plank in the shaft.[8]

Between 1861-76 the mine sold 1,025 tons of black tin, and another 230 tons in 1877 (from Mary and Trencrom.) For its later history, see under Wheal Sisters.

1. *Review of the Progress of British Mining,* December 1860
2. *Cornish Telegraph* July 16 1862
3. *Cornish Telegraph* April 17 1867
4. *Cornish Telegraph* May 11 1870
5. *Cornish Telegraph* November 22 1871
6. *Cornish Telegraph* November 5 1873
7. *Cornish Telegraph* November 4 1874
8. *Cornish Telegraph* April 7 1875

TREVA STAMPS: MENNOR STAMPS: BOWL STAMPS: TREVARRACK STAMPS: TRINK STAMPS: WESTAWAY STAMPS

In the valley that runs down from Balnoon past Bowl Rock to Lower Lelant flows a stream which formerly drove a series of water stamps. The author has vivid childhood memories of the great wheels at Mennor and Trevarrack turning ponderously amid perpetual waterfalls whilst the hills and woodlands echoed to the ear-splitting din.

In 1837 the fee-simple and inheritance in Treva Tin Stamping Mills, occupied by Messrs. Higgs & Co., were offered for sale.[1] Treva was the lowest set in the valley, being situated near Trevetho mansion. West of it lay Mennor Stamps—one had a bird's eye view of this from the road above—Bowl Stamps, Trevarrack Stamps, Trink Stamps, and Westaway Stamps.

On January 26 1860 the leases of Trink and Bowl Stamps were offered for sale by auction at the Star Hotel, Penzance. Trink possessed a water wheel and nine heads, and was in complete working order, with stamps' plots, trunks, buddles, frames, the tin on the floors, and a four-roomed dwelling house, situated in the tenements of Trink, Trevanack (*sic*) and Trevenen. The particulars relating to Bowl Stamps, with six heads, situate in the tenement of Mount Tyack, were similar. Both stamping mills were described as substantially built and well supplied with water, being capable of returning 350 tons of stuff monthly; for some years past they had been occupied by the Wheal Margaret adventurers. Enquiries were to be made of Capt. J. Hall, Wheal Margaret, or Capt. Treweeke, St. Ives.[2]

According to a later account, Trink was powered by a 28′ water wheel which worked only when sufficient water was available. During the summer months water was stored in a pool further up the valley and used when full. About 300 yards below Trink lay the eight-head set at Trevarrack, which, together with Trink, crushed material selected by hand from the dumps on Fox's section at Wheal Kitty.

Mr. Eustice, of Lelant, (b. 1853) stated in 1927 that Trevarrack Stamps were built by Capt. Dick Perry for dressing stream tin from Balnoon Bottoms. Both Trink and Trevarrack were subsequently operated by Mr. Henry Date, assisted by his son, Arthur, until about 1923, when they were taken over by the James Brothers, who paid about £3 a year in rates and £10 in rent to Tyringham. The axles and wheels belonged to him and the stamps to them. They also paid Tyringham a royalty of one load in twelve, or 1s. 6d. in the £.[3] In 1927 the West Penwith District Council, in submitting proposals for improving the Lelant and Carbis Bay water supply by abstracting water from Benny's Shute, Balnoon, offered £500 compensation for losses that would be incurred by Trink, Trevarrack, Mennor and Bowl Stamps, and soon after these wheels stopped turning.[4]

Westaway Stamps, with four heads, was set up in the croft opposite Westaway on the road going towards Trevarrack. The water was

Trencrom Mine, c. 1870. (H.)

obtained from Balnoon adit, which was blocked in order to give a sufficient head to drive the water wheel.

The hand sorted material treated at all these stamps contained about 8-10 lbs. of tin oxide per ton, and was brought from the dumps in horse drawn carts. The rock was crushed to a fine sand, the output from both Trink and Trevarrack being treated in the recovery plant at Trevarrack. This plant consisted essentially of a series of parallel long, narrow tanks, known as strips, into which the stamped sands flowed in a stream of water. The coarse tin oxide, being heavy, settled in the near end of the pit, while the light, barren sand was carried to the far end where the water and slimes flowed over a weir. This overflow from the strips carried the slime tin which settled out in a series of larger pits before the waste water and barren slime was discharged into the stream. The tin-rich end of the strip was dug out and buddled in convex circular pits where again the heavy tin oxide (cassiterite) rested at the top of the slope

Wheal Merth, near Trencrom. (G.)(M.)

and the non-tin bearing sand washed to the lower side. The concentrate from this buddling was re-buddled and finally kieved in a wooden tub to separate the valueless iron oxides from the cassiterite. This plant recovered about 14 cwt. of tin oxide every three months which was taken by horse and cart to the tin smelter at Carnkie, Redruth.

The combined stampings of the six-head Bowl Rock and eight-head Mennor Stamps were treated in the recovery plant at Mennor which was very similar to that at Trevarrack. Latterly the tin-bearing material was brought by steam wagon from the dumps at Wheal Speed at Carbis Bay, but here also work finally ceased about 1927.

1. *Royal Cornwall Gazette* July 14 1837
2. *Cornish Telegraph* January 18 1860
3. Dr. A.K. Hamilton Jenkin's notebooks, CRO, Truro
4. *Western Echo* July 8 1927

TUESDAY, JANUARY 22ND, 1867
AT NOON.

Trencrom Mine, Lelant,

NEAR THE ST. IVES ROAD STATION, ON THE WEST CORNWALL RAILWAY.

MR. JOHN THOMAS has received instructions to SELL AT PUBLIC AUCTION, at TRENCROM MINE, in the parish of Lelant, on TUESDAY, the 22nd day of JANUARY next, at twelve o'clock precisely, the following very valuable

MINE MACHINERY AND MATERIAL ;

VIZ.: —

One 30-inch 9 feet stroke BULL PUMPING ENGINE, with two Boilers, about 20 tons, complete.

One 24-inch 8 feet stroke HORIZONTAL DOUBLE WINDING ENGINE, Cage, Fly Wheel, and 10 ton Boiler, complete.

1 Capstan, Shears, 1 Angle Bob, and 1 L Bob ; 120 fathoms 1¾-inch Round Iron Horizontal Rods ; 3 Shaft Tackles, 5 tons of 9-16ths and ⅝ inch Chain ; 60 two feet Pulleys ; 40 9 feet 7 inch Pumps ; 32 9 feet 6 inch Pumps ; 3 10 feet 8 inch Pumps ; 3 10 feet 7 inch Pumps ; 1 7 feet 6 inch Pump ; 1 6 feet 7 inch Pump ; 3 11 feet 7 inch Plunger Poles, with Stuffing Boxes and Glands complete ; 3 11 feet 6 inch Plunger Poles, with Stuffing Boxes and Glands complete ; 1 7⅛-inch Plunger Pole, Stuffing Box and Gland, with H piece to match ; 1 12 feet 6 inch Working Barrel ; 1 12 feet 5 inch Working Barrel ; 2 6-inch H and top Doorpieces ; 3 5 feet 6 inch Windbores ; 1 5 feet 9 inch Windbore ; 1 3 feet 6 inch Doorpiece ; 1 5 feet 5 inch Doorpiece ; 1 8 feet 6 inch Doorpiece and Windbore ; 16 6-inch by ¾-inch thick Strapping Plates ; 64 5-inch by ⅝-inch thick ditto ; 100 fathoms of 1-inch, 7 inch, and 6-inch Main Rods ; 40 fathoms of Bucket Rods ; 200 fathoms of Ladders ; 80 fathoms of Double Skip Road ; 320 fathoms of 3¾-inch Wire Rope ; 3 Skips and 3 Tram Waggons ; 2 Horse Whims ; Shaft Tackle ; 2 Horse Whim Kibbles ; 4 pair of Blocks ; 3 small Hand Screws ; Tram Road Iron ; 200 fathoms Launders ; 1 four feet Tube, 40 feet long, for dry ; Miners' Chests ; 2 sets of Yokes ; 1 large Slate Water Tank, with tap ; Scales and Weights ; large quantity of Useful Iron in yard ; 2 Smith's Bellows ; 2 Smith's Anvils ; 2 Smith's Vices ; Screw Stock with taps, plates, and wrenches ; Smiths' and Miners' Tools ; Steel, Nails, and a variety of other articles and effects in general use in mines.

The Auctioneer would request, from Mine Agents, Founders, and the public generally who may favour him with their presence, the further favour of a punctual attendance, as the lots are numerous and the days short.

Refreshments at Twelve o'clock to the minute

Further particulars on application to the Agents on the Mine, or to the AUCTIONEER, at his Office, 1 PENRYN STREET, REDRUTH.

Dated January 9th, 1867.

Bowl Rock Stamps, Lelant in the 1920's. (D.N.)

TREVARRACK

This mine lies in granite country 300 yards north west of Beersheba Farm, Lelant. Wheal Trevarrack appears to have been first put to work during the summer of 1870, when it was described as "a young and promising enterprise." The foundation stone of its engine house was laid on June 24, a shaft, with a strong underlie, had already been sunk on the boundary of the Beersheba and Trevarrack estates to a depth of 15 fathoms. This struck an excellent lode, supposed to be a continuation of one of those which had proved so valuable in Wheal Mary. This lode was four feet wide, containing tin, whilst another lode had been discovered nearby. When the underlying shaft (Stephens') had been sunk to about 40 fms., it was expected to meet the junction of these lodes, where a rich deposit of tin should be found.

The engine house was built on Browne's shaft; it was described as a spacious structure, designed by Messrs. Michell and Jenkin of Redruth, with a stack 78 feet high, which would be a landmark for the neighbourhood. Mr. Gilbert, of Scorrier, was the builder. It was intended to house a 36″ pumping and stamping engine from North Shepherds mine, built by Sandys, Vivian & Co. from the drawings of

Messrs. Eustice & Son of Hayle. The sett had been granted by W.B. Tyringham, of Trevethoe, at 1/20th dues. It would be worked on the cost book system by Dr. Collis Browne of London and about half-a-dozen other speculators, in 2,400 shares. In their absence, the corner-stone laying ceremony was performed by Mr. Christopher Stephens of Penzance, the hope being expressed that the mine would prove a blessing to the neighbourhood.[1]

In December 1871 the shaft was reported sunk 45 fms. and it was hoped the junction of the two lodes would soon be met.[2] The career of this little enterprise came to a close in September 1876, when the materials of the "Trevarrack Mining Company, Ltd., in liquidation," were offered for sale. These included a superior 26″ (*sic*) pumping engine, 9′ stroke, with ten tons boiler; 106 fms. of 6″ to 9″ pumps; horse whim; and 230 fms. of chain.[3] As far as is known, the mine was never resumed. Its bold engine house has long since disappeared, and all that remains today of Wheal Trevarrack are a few dumps inside the footpath which runs to the north of Beersheba Farm towards Bowl Rock.

Some interesting particulars relating to the financial management of this mine were disclosed during the hearing of an alleged fraud case at Cornwall summer assizes in 1877. Mr. Lund, a retired physician, of London, claimed damages from Mr. Reynolds, a London share dealer, for fraudulent misrepresentation in regard to shares in Trevarrack which the latter had sold him. It was stated that defendant had promoted Trevarrack in 1869 as a cost-book concern. It failed utterly, no tin being obtained, and the shareholders lost all their money, among them Mr. Forster, M.P. Reynolds then turned it into a limited liability company under the name of the Trevarrack Mining Company (Limited), with a capital of £16,800 in 2,800 shares. This company was registered on October 17 1873, the bankers being Tweedy, Williams, & Co., of Redruth. Reynolds made a small advance to the company to pay two men—one to look after the engine, and the other the captain. He then induced Lund to invest £1,200 in four hundred £6 fully paid-up shares, but by a trick Reynolds secured possession of these for himself. In April 1874 he told Lund that a large outlay had been made, capital machinery erected, and the shaft sunk 60 fms. from surface, to within 20 fms. of the rich deposits of tin running into the adjacent Trencrom mine which had yielded £150,000 in profits. The shaft would be vigorously sunk to reach this rich lode. Of the £1,200 received from Dr. Lund, Reynolds put £400 into his own pocket, paid £775 into the bank, and gave £25 to a Mr. Oliver, who had assisted him in the share transaction. Of the £775, the bank claimed £250 as a liability owing to them; Reynolds took about £250 to repay money he had advanced to the mine; and £10 was paid to the secretary for expenses. In this way the money went, so that in 1876 the mine was wound up without ever having been of any use, and without raising any tin. The Judge gave a verdict for £25, without costs, holding that there was no evidence of any fraudulent intent.[4]

1. *Cornish Telegraph* June 29 1870
2. *Cornish Telegraph* December 20 1871

3. *Cornish Telegraph* September 26 1876
4. *Cornish Telegraph* July 24 1877

TREVETHOE MINE

One of the Canon's Town Valley group, Trevethoe Mine lies on the north bank of the stream, sandwiched between Wheal Merth on the west and Wheal Strawberry on the east. Although an ancient mine, little is known of its early working. A little development was carried out between 1900-5. It appears to have been sunk only to a shallow depth, the principal lode coursing about E. 20 deg. to 30 deg. N., and almost vertical, being opened upon from Engine shaft to about ten fathoms below adit. (Dines.)

TREWARTHA

The Trewartha Tin and Copper Mine, Lelant, was a slightly dishonest flotation, 1845-48. No mining was done, the property being eventually sold to another concern.

TYRINGHAM UNITED MINES

In February 1837 Francis Soddy, "auctioneer, appraiser, mine broker, and general agent," of Lelant, offered for sale by auction the materials of Tyringham United Mines, in the parish of Uny Lelant. These included a 24″ cylinder engine, double, with boiler, condensing work, axles, cranks, etc., complete, "calculated for stamping Stuff, and drawing Water." There were also three horse whims, 27 fms. of 6″ and 24 fms. of 5″ pumps; 40 fms. iron pump rods; 100 fms. horizontal rods 2¾″ by ⅝″; 100 fms. of ladders; and whim and winze kibbles. All the items were almost new, probably indicating that the mines had been at work only a short time. Enquirers were referred to Capt. Richard Blight, the managing agent, on the mine.[1]

1. *Royal Cornwall Gazette* February 17 1837

WORVAS DOWNS

This mine derives its name from Worvas Hill, one of whose summits is crowned by Knill's Steeple, a famous local landmark. The workings are centred on the S.W. section of the hill, and run into those of Balnoon; indeed, the two setts were at one time combined and worked as one. The lodes trend about N.E., being known as North Vervis ("Vervis" is an alternative spelling of Worvas) Goath, Millett's, Red (there are three of these), Mitchell's and Dog; whilst the shafts are Engine, Millett's, Dog and Harvey's. Several unnamed cross-courses traverse the sett.

The mine is an old one. In August 1812, when the effects of R. Gyles, a bankrupt, were auctioned, one of the lots comprised a sixteenth share in "Wheal Veuricas Downs Tin Mine, in the Parish of Uny Lelant." It seems to have had an intermittent career thereafter, falling idle around 1840. Then in May 1860 was issued the prospectus of "Wheal Worvas Downs Tin Mine" in 1024 £1 shares, held under lease from Messrs. Tyringham (late Praed) and others, at 1-18th dues, Mr. James Hollow, of Lelant, being purser. It lay on the same run of lodes as Providence and Trelyon Consols on the W., with St. Ives Consols and Rosewall Hill to the N., and Wheal Reeth, Wheal Margaret, Wheal Kitty and others to the S. The workings were about 70 fms. under adit, the stratum being the tin-producing granite of the district. The sett extended about 800 fms. from E. to W. and 400 fms. from N. to S.

"The great success of all the other old Tin Mines recently re-opened in this district. . . and the excellent opinion of various parties who worked in this Mine 20 years ago, coupled with the present high price of Tin, as compared with the price paid at the last working, point this out as one of the best Adventures in the neighbourhood. This Mine when last worked formed a part of the ancient 'Balnoon' Mines (at one time enormously rich), and was worked by flat rods therefrom. They had no steam power on it either for drawing the stuff or pumping, consequently as it became deep the workings became more expensive and difficult to carry on. The drawing power was a Whim drawn by four Horses (a most unusual number), and even that means became inadequate to do the work. Just at this point the other workings in the extensive sett became poor, and as this part could not be carried on without an outlay for machinery it was abandoned."

They proposed to erect a suitable pumping engine with stamps combined, and as the water in the district was very easy, one of 30″ cylinder would probably be found sufficient. A separate steam winding engine would also be erected. The mine was known to contain carbonas of good quality from which profitable returns could be made as soon as it was properly opened, besides others only partially developed. "The working of these it is expected will be highly remunerative, as the large profits paid by the 'Providence Mines' adjoining are from precisely similar deposits. In fact, analogy, position and circumstances are greatly in favour of this becoming one of the prizes of the district." An outlay of £5-6,000 was deemed sufficient to bring it into a paying state.

Regarding this promotion, the *Cornish Telegraph* of July 11 following stated that one of the largest shareholders in St. Ives Consols had recently asked the oldest agent in that mine, Capt. T. Mitchell, to examine and report on Worvas Downs. Mitchell described how in the eastern part of the sett, some half century ago, the burrows were worked by the Daniels, of St. Ives. "The tin stuff was so rich that they carried home each day's produce in bags in the evening—tin selling at £35 per ton that would now bring from £80 to £90. In this beautiful rich tin ground district it would be quite in place to mention that Kemp's lode, in St. Ives Consols, from which has been raised from £60—70,000 worth tin and copper, crosses the Worvas sett. My opinion is that the Worvas Downs sett is one of the best pieces of mineral property in the western district, and I have not the least doubt of its making a lasting dividend-paying mine.'' Encouraged by this favourable assessment, a group of adventurers prosecuted the mine with vigour, Capt. T. Richards being appointed manager at £2 2s. a month in March 1861.

However, the four-monthly account issued in September 1862 showed a debit balance of £461 3s. 11d., and a 12s. call was levied in November. Capt. Harry reported that the pitwork and machinery, including the new water stamps, were in good working condition, no further outlay on them being required. They had 41 persons employed underground and at surface. The venture does not seem to have been financially very rewarding, but there were recorded sales of tin between 1862-4. The Stannary Court records (at the County Record Office, Truro) show that when Richard Oliver, the bailiff, sent in his inventory of materials to the liquidator, he wrote: "It is a bad Place for getting letters, if they are directed to the Mine they will be carried to Lelant and there left until called for, it is a good distance from the Mine.''

In 1905 the mine was re-opened with Capt. C.C. Millett, of Lelant, in charge. In October about 30 men were employed at "the promising little Vervas mine, near Knill's Steeple,'' enough tin being raised from shallow workings to pay expenses. Engine shaft was down 60 fms.[1] This adventure was run privately by Lord Armstrong and Mr. F.E. de Mattos. The sett was an extensive one, comprising the old Balnoon Mines and Westaway. In July 1906 they were said to be raising some splendid tin from the 60 fm. level.[2] Five tons of tin were sent for ticketing in June 1907. In October the stamps were idle, attention being directed entirely to development. Four lodes were being worked, three trending E. and W. and the other a caunter. Main lode averaged over 3′ in width and inclined N. 70 deg.; it had been driven nearly 700′ in either direction, and maintained its normal value in depth. Valuable reserves were being created on Millett's lode, while on South lode a new incline shaft had been sunk 100 fms., this being the same depth as the central working. The average yield of all produce was about 27 lbs. of tin per ton. The machinery included a double cylinder self-condensing horizontal engine of 150 h.p. for driving a ten heads California stamps, a stone crusher, powerful winding gear and a small air compressor, all of which, together with an Evans pump, were supplied from one marine and two vertical Cochran boilers. There was also another horizontal engine at the new shaft for hoisting. The modern milling plant could deal with about thirty tons daily. Some curious stones recently discovered on the mine had evidently been used by the ancients for treating tin.[3] The epitaph of this undertaking was written by Collins, who stated that it yielded nothing except for the lawyers.

1. *St. Ives Weekly Summary* October 7 1905
2. *St. Ives Weekly Summary* July 7 1906
3. *Western Echo* October 26 1907

SECOND SECTION
MORVAH DISTRICT

CARN GALVER (WHEAL ROSE): MORVAH HILL (FRISTEN):
MORVAH AND ZENNOR UNITED
GARDEN MINE
MORVAH CONSOLS
WHEAL WHIDDEN

CARN GALVER (WHEAL ROSE): MORVAH HILL (FRISTEN): MORVAH AND ZENNOR UNITED

One of the most picturesque features seen along the beautiful St. Ives—Land's End coast road is the group of ruined buildings belonging to the old Morvah and Zennor United mine, near the hamlet of Rosemergy. Backed in one direction by rugged cliffs and the sea and on the other by the bracken-covered hills and moors of the West Penwith peninsula, these gaunt structures, battered by more than a century of Atlantic gales, stand as silent memorials to the hardy race who delved for tin in this remote section of Cornwall.

Morvah and Zennor United comprises Morvah Hill, Carn Galver (Wheal Rose) and the smaller workings of Wheals Whidden, Goth, Grous, Land and Fristen. Some of these ancient mines are mentioned in an indenture dated January 1 1742 and renewed on March 31 1764, being "3-4ths of 1-3rd of 5 pair tin bounds, Whele Goath, Whele an Grouse, Whele Whidden, Whele Langand, Whele an Frillen, Carnon within Trevian Downs, Morvah; 3-4ths of 1-3rd of 3 pair bounds, Whele an Strepan (two not named), Carnan Vyth in Trevyan Downs, Morvah." (Per Justin Brooke.)

In October 1836 Mr. Samuel Higgs, the purser of "Morvah and Zennor Tin Mines," advertised for an agent—"none need apply who are not well acquainted with Tinnery and are in other respects fully competent to undertake the Situation, and who will reside on or near the Mines, and devote their time and attention to its concerns."[1] This residential stipulation would have deterred many from applying, Zennor being very unpopular with mine captains by reason of its isolation. The mine was working on a fairly considerable scale at this time, Henwood stating in 1838 that it employed 116 persons. One of these employees, a miner named John Newton, was seriously injured in May 1840 when a hole he was charging with powder exploded and "blew both eyes out."[2] Between 1837-9 195 tons of black tin were sold.

This period of working came to an end in August 1840 when the materials, described as nearly new and in good condition, were put up for sale by auction. They included "an excellent 40-inch Cylinder *Steam*

Headgear, Worvas Downs, 1904. (E.M.)

Engine, eight feet stroke, with Cast-Iron *Beam,* and about 9 tons Boiler complete, (it will be seen by reference to 'Lean's Monthly Engine Reporter,' that this Engine does the best duty of any in her class in the County)." There were also a very large water wheel, 60′ in diameter and 2′ breast, with iron axle; three balance bobs; four horse whims; a ton of horse whim chain; a superior capstan and shears; and 150 fms. of 9″ capstan rope.[3]

In 1851 the Carn Galver property was acquired by a company headed by John Coulson, which commenced to drive an adit from the cliff towards the hill which gives the mine its name, with the twin objectives of facilitating drainage and discovering new lodes. They also set men to work rehabilitating and developing the higher levels of the mine. This was situated about 280 fms. from the brow of the Morvah and Zennor cliff, and had been worked on a rather extensive scale by the former adventurers to a depth of 60 fms. The new company proposed to drive their adit from the base of the cliff at high water mark, which was at a depth of 70 fms. below surface at the old engine house.

In March 1851 the *Mining Journal* reported the adit already driven 37 fms. southward from the sea. Moor shaft had been collared and ladders put in to (the old) adit, a horse whim erected on Roscorla's shaft and the shaft itself secured to adit. (Old) adit level had been cleared 97 fms. W. from Roscorla's and men put to drive on the Ranger lode with the object of reaching Heathcock lode, of which good accounts had been heard. Preparations were in hand to clear the 10 fm. level under adit of water, where the last men who worked there said tin could be immediately broken. By driving a short distance from this level the productive Tregwarra tin lode would be cut. Several men were waiting to take up the pitches they had previously worked when the mine was operating under the name of Morvah and Zennor. From Heathcock (or Heathcote) lode they intended driving to cut the Osborne lode, formerly famous for tin. At this point they would have an adit 50 fms. from grass on Ranger lode, whilst the new deep adit would come in 50 fms. below this.

By May, Roscorla's shaft had been cleared 18 fms. below adit on Ranger lode, and tin broken in the 10 fm. level below adit. Sea level on the cross-course (in the new adit) had a very kindly appearance, there being a large stream of water proceeding from the end, always considered a good sign, and it was expected that one of the E. and W. lodes would soon be encountered.

By 1855 the new adit had been driven 250 fms. from its entrance in a straight line towards the nearest and deepest shaft of the mine. Ventilation of the first 160 fms. had been effected in the following manner:- A stream of water was allowed to fall through a perpendicular wood pipe 12″ square and 10 fms. in length, whose lower end was inserted a few inches below the surface of an open trough of water at the adit entrance. A wooden air pipe, 4″ square, was let into the side of the perpendicular pipe 4′ above its lower end and extended from there through the whole length of the adit. The rush of water through the perpendicular pipe, escaping over the sides of the trough, forced a continuous current of air through the air pipe into the adit, which proved effectual for 160 fms., when it began to fail. The miners nevertheless succeeded in driving the level a further 90 fms. despite having to contend with an increasingly bad atmosphere, but were then obliged to desist, as the air in the end would support neither life nor combustion.

Mr. John Coulson, jun., of Penzance, then tried the following experiment:- A half-inch pipe of gutta percha, 320 fms. long, was laid on the side of the cliff near a stream of water about 30 fms. above the adit entrance and carried over the cliff into its end. The pipe's external end was inserted into the middle of a narrow wood launder with sides half-an-inch high, over which passed as much water as it could convey. The stream poured into the pipe with great rapidity, and as the quantity of water which passed over its opening was not sufficient to fill it, a deep vortex was formed, and so a continuous stream of air mixed with water was drawn through the entire length of the pipe and discharged at the end of the adit with considerable force.

The experiment was most successful. After allowing the current to flow 12 hours, the Captain and some men went into the end and were delighted to find that their candles burned brightly and that they could breathe freely.

Mr. Coulson then re-designed his apparatus, so as to increase the air supply by allowing the water introduced with it to escape via a separator. The new appliance consisted of a launder; a trough placed on the brow of the cliff; and a "Hydro-Pneumatic Box" set at one side of the adit entrance, 30 fms. below the trough; air and water pipes connected the trough and box; and two glass tubes, open at each end, to serve as a regulator, were suspended over the latter. By adjusting the glass tubes, a partial vacuum was created in the air and water pipes, and a continuous current of air and water (in the proportion of nine parts air to 6 of water) conveyed from the trough to the box. In this box the air and water were separated, the water being removed by a pipe fitted with a stop cock to control its pressure. The air was forced through a "ventilating tube" at the top of the box, and could be taken to any distance, as the pressure obtained was very great.

When the air pipe was being carried into the end at Carn Galver the atmosphere was so foul as to be incapable of keeping candles alight, and the men handling it had to find their way in perfect darkness, but soon after the apparatus was set to work, six miners were sent into the end, each having a candle burning, when it was found that the current of pure air discharged from the pipe was so strong that it instantly blew out three candles held together four feet away. Work in the adit was then able to proceed uninterruptedly, the men being provided with an excellent supply of fresh air, whereas previously a candle could not be kept burning, nor a match ignited, "nor could the men work, or breathe, except with painful difficulty, although all the means and appliances known in this County had been tried."

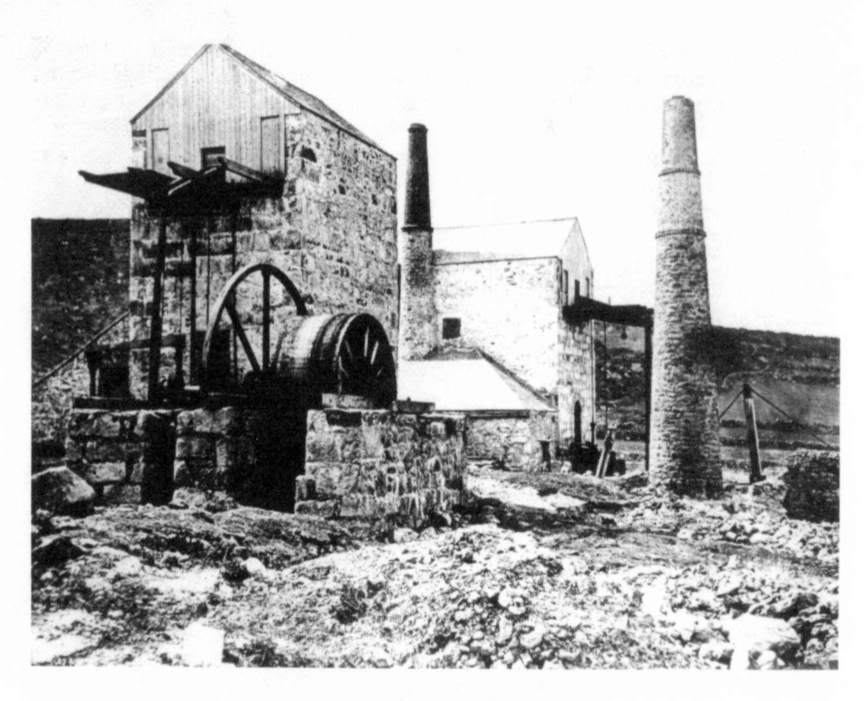

Carn Galver Mine, 1885. (J.H.T.)

The apparatus was inspected by Capt. John Truran, of Ding Dong mine, who, in a report dated September 19 1855, spoke in eulogistic terms of its advantages and beneficial effects. He noted how easily the workmen could regulate the air supply by a slight adjustment of the glass tubes, and was particularly impressed by the superiority of the gutta percha air pipe to the wooden pipes hitherto used. "The machine with wooden pipes has several insuperable disadvantages." he wrote. "The pipes can be seldom more than 3 fms. in length, which are roughly fitted, by spigot and faucet. These require to be luted on, which is uniformly done with clay, brought to a consistence for the purpose, but as it is not impervious to water, soon falls off, leaving the joints open, for the escape of air, or admission of water, both of which are equally fatal to the due transmission of air to the point required."

He concluded: "Mr. Coulson's machine is now working with a small stream of water, discharging more than 1,000 gallons of pure air per hour at a distance from the Hydro-Pneumatic box of not less than 240 or 250 fms.; at the same time, from the velocity with which the air is discharged at the end, and the force required to stop the jet at the end of the pipe, the machine has still in reserve sufficient power to carry air beyond anything that may be required in mining."

Joseph Wallis, writing on behalf of the committee of Carn Galver adventurers, congratulated Mr. Coulson on his machine, stating that had it not been for this invention, the work at Carn Galver must have been abandoned, or else ventilating shafts sunk with great labour and expense.

The invention was, indeed, widely hailed as a significant advance in mining technology, which would enable long levels to be driven with greater speed and cheapness, and having immense potential for improving the health of miners working in "close" ends with no adequate means of ventilation. Details of it were communicated to the Secretary of the Royal Cornwall Polytechnic Society at Falmouth, whilst a working model was placed on display at Mr. Coulson's house in Chapel Street, Penzance, where those interested in mining matters were invited to inspect it.[4]

The appliance certainly proved invaluable in driving the Carn Galver adit level, the completion of whose final stages, however, was attended with considerable danger to the workmen engaged on it. The mine towards which the level was being driven contained a vast quantity of accumulated water, which had risen to surface. The adit, driven S. on a cross-course or soft channel of ground, was equipped with a tram-road for the removal of stuff, and operations continued gradually and perseveringly for about five years, the work being beset by numerous difficulties and interruptions, until at length water was seen to spurt out from cracks in the side of the level. These gradually increased in quantity, so that "even the stout-hearted shrugged their shoulders and became alarmists on the question of the propriety of any miner risking his life further."

Very cautiously, however, the driving was resumed, a long iron bar being inserted 4-6 ft. in advance of the end in the solid rock. "The result of these operations may be termed a marvellous success, as it happened that the iron bar eventually bored into the side of the bottom level of the old mine as perfectly as if it had been all dialled and measured to a fathom of ground! The miners had ample time afforded them to beat a retreat. Thus, a vast body of water, say about 400' deep and near 1,000' long, gradually disgorged itself into the ocean without being attended by either loss of life or the slightest casualty."[5] The completion of this adit, well over a quarter of a mile in length, in the face of many difficulties, from the formidable cliffs in a remote and wild region of West Cornwall, surely ranks as one of the most memorable mining achievements by the "old men" of the mid-19th century.

A new hydraulic engine was installed in 1858, the cost of which put the June account seriously in the red.[6] They were still in debt in September, despite a small item on the credit side of 15s. 9d. for "gunpowder casks returned."[7] During March quarter of 1859 they just met cost, a tiny profit of £2 4s. being recorded. Tin sold amounted to 11 tons 16 cwt., an increase of 1 ton 17 cwt. on the previous quarter. The debit balance had been wiped off, as well as expenses incurred in exploring Rosemergy cliff.[8] By September things were looking so well

Ruins of Carn Galver Mine. (W.T.)

that they were able to declare a dividend of 10s. per share.

The meeting for September 1860 was informed that about £100 had been spent clearing up and timbering Engine shaft and enlarging "Bossigran" stamps. A new double-acting steam engine had been delivered by Messrs. Harvey & Co., and when erected, preparations would be made for working a skip through Anneal shaft. During the progress of this work, which would last four or five weeks, hauling would have to be suspended, and the broken tribute and tutwork stuff stored in the levels until the skip was operating. The 80 fm. level had been driven 28 fms. E. from Anneal shaft through unproductive ground; it was close to the point of intersection of the South lode where tin had been found at all the higher levels. The 70 had been driven 75 fms. E., the lode here being split and disordered. The 60, driven 117 fms. E., was producing good stones of tin. The North and South lode at the 60 had been driven on S. 40 fms.; the lode in the end being disorganised by a cross-course of spar. This lode had also been driven on S. from the 40 fm. level, with the twin object of exploring and, by a winze, ventilating the 60 fm. level, where good tribute ground was opened but could not be worked through lack of air.[9]

The December account for 1861 showed that expenditure on permanent work during the previous 18 months had been very high, and included the cost of the new 30″ double-acting engine; timbering Anneal shaft and putting in the skip with poppet head and tramway, superseding the horse whims; retimbering Engine shaft and equipping both shafts with pumps and balance bobs; erecting a 36′ water wheel with a new set of twelve heads of stamps; and installing two new patent Borlase's round buddles, 20′ in diameter, representing a total outlay of about £4,000. Of this amount, £950 had been supplied by calls and the remainder by profits. A second water wheel and further dressing equipment had still to be provided. It was anticipated the Borlase's buddles would greatly reduce the labour cost of dressing both strip and slime work by as much as 40%; already much fine tin was being saved by this process which previously had gone to waste.[10]

Unfortunately, in September 1869 it was found necessary to offer the materials for sale, the mine having been stopped in consequence of the recent low price for tin and the failing health of the lessee and principal shareholder. The lords had offered to grant a new 21 years' lease to any responsible person or company. Interested persons were invited to apply for a viewing to Matthew Eddy, timberman. The mine had returned nearly £26,000 worth of tin during the late working.[11]

A new company was formed to take up the Carn Galver setts in March 1871, the shareholders being from West Cornwall. They were encouraged in this venture by a statement to the effect that just before the 1869 stoppage an excellent tin lode had been cut in the 90 fm. level, supposed to be an entirely new discovery in unwrought ground.[12] In November G. Eustice & Son, engineers, of Hayle, were stated to be erecting three engines on the mine—a 40″ pumping, a 30″ stamping and a 20″ whim. An 1873 directory discloses that this mine, described as the

"Carn Galver Tin Mine, Zennor. . . on the border of the parish of Zennor, adjoining Morvah, 3 miles from Zennor Churchtown and 6 from Penzance, the nearest shipping place and railway station," was held under a 21 year lease from 1871 at 1-20th dues. Adit level was 70 fms. below surface, the shaft being 130 fms. deep. The ore was crushed by a compound steam engine fitted with two pneumatic stamps, which would do the work of sixteen of the ordinary kind. There was a considerable accumulation of water, which was being pumped out by steam power. Since May 1871 about 15 tons of ore had been raised; when the water was reduced, about 12-15 tons would be raised per month. The work force totalled 70. The company (of limited liability) was in 10,000 £1 shares, the purser being Thomas Willis Field and the manager John Roach.

This new company did not have a long life, and by December of that year was in liquidation, the setts and materials being put up for sale in January 1874. The advertisement issued at that time referred to a 30″ pumping engine with 10 tons boiler; 22″ winder with 7 tons boiler, and cage; and a 17″ high pressure compound engine, with 10 tons boiler and two heads of Husband's patent pneumatic stamps.[13] The mine was bought by Messrs. Bolitho & Co. and Messrs. Michell & Co. for £1,600, but appears soon afterwards to have been closed.

Turning to Morvah Hill Mine, it is interesting to note that this is situated at one of the highest elevations of any mine in West Cornwall, Engine shaft being above the 700′ contour, 370 yards W. of the summit of Watch Croft. An early reference to one of its constituents, Fristen, lying to the N.N.W., occurs in a bounds agreement made on August 20 1785 which gave Edward Edwards, tinner, of St. Just, permission to search for tin throughout "a certain pair of Tin Bounds called the Fristen or Fruiting Bounds situate. . . in the tenement of Rosemergy in the parish of Morvah in Penwith." He was required to work them with a minimum of two men, the dues being 1-15th to the lord and 1-10th to the bounders. The document was witnessed by Jno. Pearce and "Meartine thomas." On March 1 1787 the owners of two pairs of tin bounds called the Great Fristen or Fruiting Bounds, and the Little Fristen or Horne's Bounds in the parish of Morvah, granted Edward Mann, of Zennor, permission to work that portion of them running "from the tail of the addit which he has already begun to clear so far to Hill as both the said Bounds extend," at similar dues.[14]

It appears that soon after Carn Galver, in Zennor, was resumed in 1871, the neighbouring, similarly named sett in Morvah was taken up and worked by a separate but associated company. The 1873 Post Office Directory, previously quoted, refers to the "Carn Galver Tin Mine, Morvah," held under a 21 year lease granted by Henry White at 1-20th dues, reopened by the present adventurers in 1872. It was a cost-book concern, the officers being the same persons as those named in connection with the Zennor Carn Galver. There were said to be four known lodes in the sett, and several cross-courses, the dip being 2′ 6″ in a fathom. The mine was worked and drained by a 30″ steam engine.

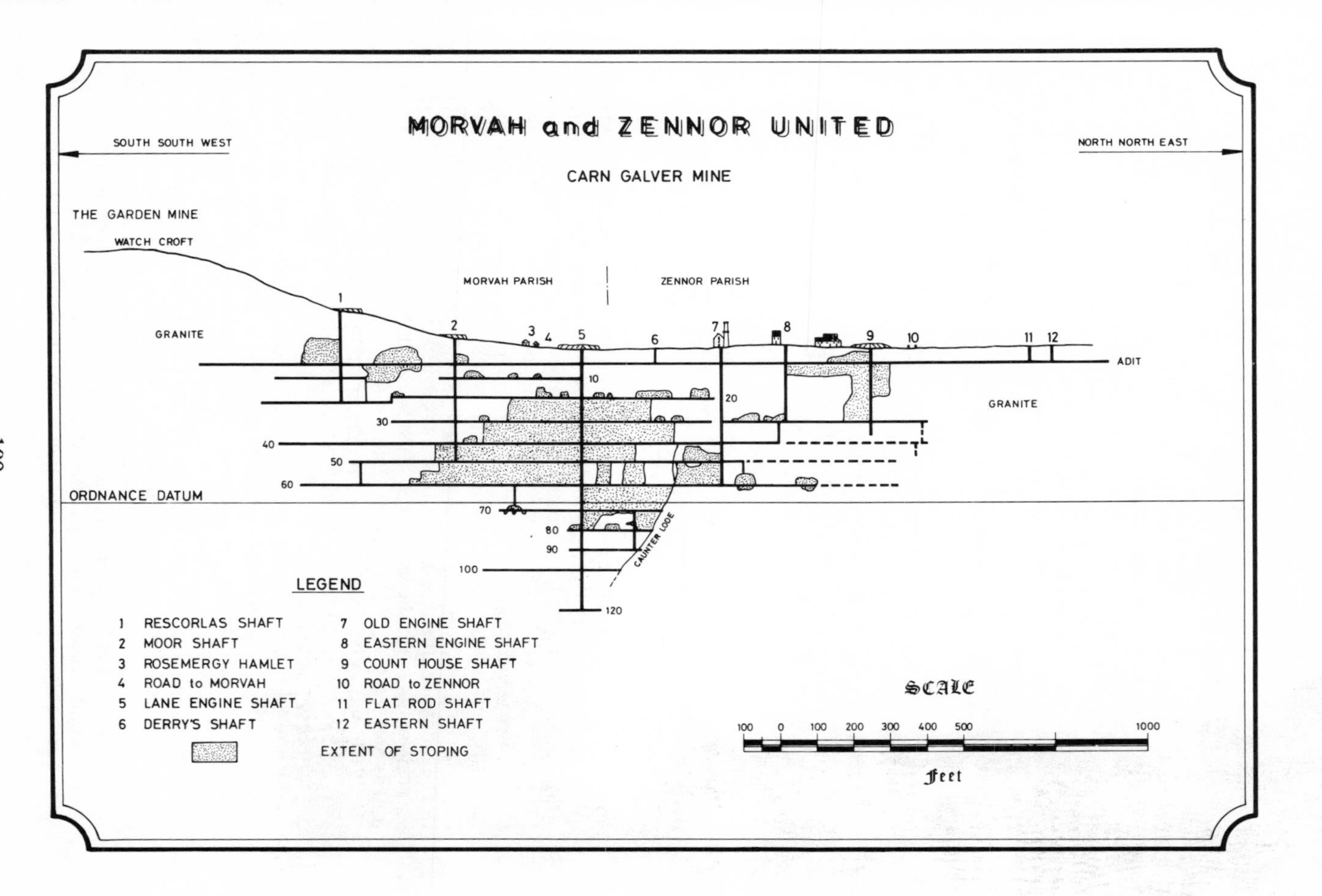
MORVAH and ZENNOR UNITED
CARN GALVER MINE
SOUTH SOUTH WEST
NORTH NORTH EAST
THE GARDEN MINE
WATCH CROFT
MORVAH PARISH
ZENNOR PARISH
GRANITE
GRANITE
ADIT
ORDNANCE DATUM
CAUNTER LODE
10
20
30
40
50
60
70
80
90
100
120
LEGEND
1 RESCORLAS SHAFT
2 MOOR SHAFT
3 ROSEMERGY HAMLET
4 ROAD to MORVAH
5 LANE ENGINE SHAFT
6 DERRY'S SHAFT
7 OLD ENGINE SHAFT
8 EASTERN ENGINE SHAFT
9 COUNT HOUSE SHAFT
10 ROAD to ZENNOR
11 FLAT ROD SHAFT
12 EASTERN SHAFT
EXTENT OF STOPING
SCALE
100 0 100 200 300 400 500 1000
Feet

Worvas Downs. (H.C.C.)(L.E.C.)

1. *Royal Cornwall Gazette* October 28 1836
2. *Penzance Gazette* May 20 1840
3. *West Briton* August 7 1840
4. *Cornish Telegraph* October 10 1855
5. *Cornish Telegraph* April 10 1867
6. *Royal Cornwall Gazette* June 5 1858
7. *Royal Cornwall Gazette* September 24 1858
8. *Royal Cornwall Gazette* June 24 1859
9. *Cornish Telegraph* December 12 1860
10. *Cornish Telegraph* March 5 1862
11. *Cornish Telegraph* September 1869
12. *Cornish Telegraph* March 8 1871
13. *Cornish Telegraph* January 7 1874
14. MS per G.C. Penaluna, Wheal Rose Coach Works, Scorrier

GARDEN MINE

The Garden Mine formed part of the Morvah and Zennor United complex, and exploited the Osborne lode, one of the four major lodes of the United sett, trending, like the other three (Black, Lang and Clukey) in a N.N.W. direction; it extends from the hilly inland part to pass under the coast road and crops out in the cliff at Carn Osborne, where it is crossed by Rosemergy Cliff lode, coursing about N.E.

In December 1859 it was announced that the Garden Mine, in the parish of Morvah, owned by Samuel Borlase, Esq., of Castle Horneck, was about to be re-opened by Mr. R. White, the purser of Pendeen Consols. It had been worked many years before as a "free sett," and the miners earned a considerable amount of money. In view of the various lodes which underlay towards and ran across this sett, and its congenial strata, it was thought the chances of permanent success were good.[1] By 1861 the mine was 25 fms. deep and employed 20 persons.[2] In March of the following year a call of £5 was made, only 1 ton 12 cwt. of tin having been sold during the quarter. The agents recommended sinking a shaft in the centre of the workings in the higher part of the mine, which offered the best chance of success, and this was agreed to. The purser stated that several agents from the leading St. Just mines had inspected the workings and expressed a very favourable opinion of the higher section.[3]

Production during the March quarter of 1863 amounted to 4 tons 8 cwt. of black tin, which realised (less dues) £279. The mine was then in debt, necessitating a £4 call, but there were two tons of tin in stock which could not be sold for want of stamping power; if returned, this would about enable them to meet cost, and the agent's report was of a rather favourable character. It was decided to subdivide the 114 shares into 1,026ths.[4]

The mine sold 14¾ tons of tin in the December 1865 quarter, and almost succeeded in balancing the books. The 24 fm. level was driving N. on a new lode, discovered when driving E. on Thomas's lode, by two men at £2 10s. per fm., lode worth £8. 11 pitches were working on tribute by 38 men at tributes ranging from 12s. to 19s. in the £. The shareholders were agreeably surprised to find their prospects so good when those of other mines were gloomy.[5] In November, Capt. John White reported that a shaft had been cleared up from surface and sunk to the 24 fm. level on the new lode. The 36 level was driving E. of Engine shaft on Thomas's lode at £4 4s. per fm., lode worth £2. The level was also driving N. on the cross-lode at £2 12s. 6d. per fm., lode worth £1 10s., and S. on the same lode at £3 10s. per fm., lode worth £2 10s. The new shaft was sunk in the centre of the tin ground in this part of the mine, and would be of great advantage in ventilating and for discharging stuff. 42 men and 8 boys were employed, and 7 tribute pitches being worked. The purser stated that about £6,000 had been spent on development, and the undertaking was looked upon by mining critics as a very promising speculation. Hopes were expressed that they would soon fall in with some of those rich deposits which in recent years had been so prolific in neighbouring Ding Dong.[6]

In 1867 the adventurers acquired part of the Rosemergy sett, the other portion being added to the Boswednan mine. According to Purser White, several of the Garden lodes intersected in the Rosemergy sett, which had formerly been worked by Carn Galver. Rosemergy adit lay 30 fms. below the Garden adit, and the addition of this piece of ground not only considerably enlarged the area to be worked by the Garden adventurers, but would drain their mine almost to the bottom, so that the engine would be idle for some time. Rosemergy sett extended inland from the cliff between Carn Galver and the Garden for a long distance. The agent (Capt. John White) reported the 12 fm. level driving E. of Engine shaft on the Ranger lode by four men at £2 per fm., lode worth £3. The new shaft had been sunk to the 36 fm. level through good ground, and that level driven several fathoms on the new lode E. and W. of the shaft; but as the adit in the new Rosemergy section lay 24 fms. (*sic*) deeper than the Garden adit, and nearly ran into these workings, it had been thought best to suspend them in order to clear up the deep adit and effect a communication with the new shaft. This adit had already been cleared for 150 fms., and they hoped to make the junction within two months, when work on the new lode would be resumed with great vigour.[7]

Although the mine had lapsed into a calling state by September 1868 the adventurers nevertheless resolved that the deep adit or sea level be driven under the old workings on Wheal Osborne, the lode being about 18 fms. distant. This was on the understanding that the purser's salary should be reduced during the exploration to a guinea per month and the agent's to four guineas per month. Capt. John White reported that they had driven adit level about 12 fms. on the new lode, which had produced a little tin but not in payable quantities. They had also sunk a winze and stoped some ground in the bottom of this level which had just about paid for itself. The 12 fm. level E. of Engine shaft was driven to the Heathcock lode and opened 4 fms. on it; the lode was small and poor. Osborne lode having presented a very favourable appearance at adit level, they had sunk a winze about 7 fms. below it, three of which were in good paying ground, the lode being worth £3 per fm., which could be

RARE OPPORTUNITY FOR INVESTMENT IN

Cornish Mining.

TO BE SOLD BY AUCTION, on Friday, the 3rd day of September next, by 12 o'clock at noon, at CARN GALVER MINE, in the parish of Zennor, in the following or such other lots as may then be determined on, the very valuable

MACHINERY AND MINE MATERIALS

THEREON:—

LOT 1.—30-inch double-action steam engine, with 2 bobs for pumping and drawing; 9 tons' boiler; pumps and other pitwork; whim chain; pullies; skip road, &c., &c.

LOT 2.—12-head water stamps, with 36-feet water wheel, erected with the best materials, and at a very considerable expense.

IN SUNDRY LOTS.—New and old iron; steel; miners' tools; contents of blacksmith's shop; the account-house furniture; Norway balk; scales and weights; miner's dial; the necessary materials used in tin cleaning at the stamps, including a Borlase's patent buddle.

The Lords have offered to grant a new lease for 21 years to any responsible person or company. The mine has returned near £26,000 worth of tin, and was stopped in consequence of the late low price, coupled with the failing health of the present lessee and principal shareholder. As a speculation it forms one of the most promising concerns in the market.

The whole may be viewed on application to MATTHEW EDDY, timber-man, on the mine.

REFRESHMENTS AT 11 A.M.

For further particulars apply to

JOHN PERMEWAN,
Auctioneer.

Penzance, 21st Aug., 1869.

stoped for £1 5s. However, it had now declined; and in consequence of water difficulties they proposed to suspend it, considering the drivage of the deep adit would afford better proof of the lode's productiveness. A further outlay of £150 would give it a satisfactory trial.[8] The basic reason for this decision appears to have been the fact that the "hilly" (inland) part of the mine had become unproductive. A year later it was reported that about 20 fms. of tribute ground had been opened in the adit level. Some machinery was then being moved to this section, which it was hoped would become the nucleus of a permanent and profitable mine. Sadly, this expectation was not realised, the Garden falling a victim to the mining depression which set in soon after.

1. *Royal Cornwall Gazette* December 16 1859
2. Williams, J., *Cornwall & Devon Mining Directory,* 1861
3. *Cornish Telegraph* March 5 1862
4. *Royal Cornwall Gazette* June 19 1863
5. *Cornish Telegraph* March 26 1866
6. *Cornish Telegraph* November 7 1866
7. *Cornish Telegraph* July 3 and 10 1867
8. *Cornish Telegraph* September 9 1868

MORVAH CONSOLS

The ruined engine house of Morvah Consols picturesquely stands a short distance from the cliff north of Morvah parish church. On the verge of these granite cliffs and in the scattered islets beneath several lodes may be seen, which the "old men" exploited by driving an adit into the hill just above the reach of the sea and sinking a shaft some distance below that level. The lodes produced excellent tinstone, but before much profit could be obtained rising water compelled the abandonment of these workings. Subsequently, several partially successful efforts were made by speculators to develop the sett. A company was formed for this purpose around the year 1830; whilst in the early 1850's the mine was taken up by a Mr. Daniel, of St. Ives.

Then, in 1872, James Hammon, a Londoner, who had previously held the position of secretary to Great North Tolgus (1859), secretary to West Dolcoath (1858) and purser to the latter mine (1861), successfully concluded negotiations with the lords (Messrs. H. and R. White, of Bojewyan) to re-open Morvah Consols. A company was formed and some preliminary exploration carried out. In July the 13 fm. level on Black lode, east of Whiteburrow shaft, was reported 2′ wide with excellent stones of tin.[1] From the middle of 1873 development was speeded up, but a near disaster resulted when the miners holed into ancient workings. In November, A.C. Wildman, the indefatigable editor and mining correspondent of the *Cornish Telegraph,* visited Morvah Consols and wrote a graphic account of the mine, from which the following has been condensed:

"This sett lies in the tenement of Trevowan, the main part of the present workings being between Zawn Alley and the Wolf, two well-defined points on the cliff, and on the Black-burrow lode, which traverses them in a N.E.-S.W. direction. A little to the N.E. of the last of the famous group of St. Just mines and within this tenement of Trevowan are several lodes—the Island, the Grebe, and the Venton Join—all intersected by Wheal Neptune cross-course, some of them visible to the veriest tyro in geology as they crop out at sea level and show their distinctive features as they pass inland. It was to disinter these that the 'old men', with infinite pains and excellent judgement, drove the level by which the workings are entered.

"At surface a little account or changing house has been built, and a neat engine house is erecting—the latter for a 24" pumping, stamping and drawing engine bought at Balleswidden, which it is hoped may be at work by Christmas. The exposed site, the bad weather, and the difficulty of procuring labour, have retarded construction, but it is to be pushed on with all possible speed. Surface men are busy at two shafts' mouths, adding to the 800 sacks of ore already raised. The carpenters are fixing together massive framework for the shafts; the smith, in his comfortable little smithy, makes the sparks fly and the anvil ring; miners pass to and fro, for the blacksmiths' shop is, as yet, the only changing and tool house; and the coast margin, long left to the goat and the rabbit, is once more the scene of activity and enterprise.

"Descending the acclivity by a pathway which winds through the furze and rocks one reaches a pile of light-coloured 'deads.' Some of the larger stones have rolled down to the sea, washed down when the present miners holed their predecessors' workings, and ran through the adit for their lives, as the long pent-up water chased them in a torrent through the level. The adit at first traverses decomposing granite. Two or three air holes, from 20 to 30 ft. deep, were put in by the old men from surface, and provide so much illumination as to make candles of little service. But beyond them lies harder ground—partially decomposed granite studded with angular stones—whilst further in still is the solid rock, the passage now ankle-deep in water, and dark, so that candles now come into their own.

"Soon there are signs of the Black-burrow lode. The former workers followed it up from here to grass, using their timber sparingly, and filling up the space vacated by the lode with deads. This material must have compacted well, for only two or three sodden, decayed slabs now keep up the mass, and these so rotten that pieces may be squeezed out of them as if they were touch-wood. Eventually the spot is reached where the old workings were holed, and then the shaft, here 16 fms. from surface, but with a further downward continuation filled with water and protected by a firm sollar. This it will be the work of the engine to drain and keep dry. The lode is being worked on by three points, each yielding specimens of tin. The lode retains its good qualities as it goes down; and it is evident that as the bal is sunk there is every chance of this lode being made remunerative, as well as of discovering others."[2]

The bad weather experienced that winter at this exposed site caused such serious delays in erecting the engine house that the engine could not be set to work until March 10 1874. This had originally been made at

Hayle by Sandys, Vivian & Co. On being removed from Balleswidden, it was overhauled by G. Eustice & Son, engineers, also of Hayle, and Holman's Foundry, of St. Just, and fitted with a new cylinder. The engine was self-acting, with a 9′ stroke, the total cost being around £600. At the colourful christening ceremony, Mr. Hammon, chief sponsor of the new venture, stepped out on to the platform beside the engine bob and cracking a bottle of wine across its iron nose named the engine "Holland's," after Col. Holland, chairman of the directors, and the shaft "Hammon's" to mark his own interest in the mine. An engineer simultaneously opened a valve and the bob, living up to its name, made its first bow to the forty guests who had been invited to the ceremony. The pumps soon filled with water, which splashed along the launders; the stamps wheel on the other side of the house began to revolve, and the whole of the machinery was soon working smoothly and well. The guests were then invited to an excellent meal which had been laid out for them in the carpenters' shop, temporarily converted into a dining room. Only a few days after the engine was started a young lad from St. Just followed a rabit into the fly-wheel pit, the machine then being at rest; the engine-driver, ignorant of his presence, set it in motion, but the boy, with great presence of mind, clutched one of the fly-wheel's arms, and in this perilous position was carried round with it until the cries of his companions caused the driver to stop the engine. His clothes were torn to pieces, and he was badly cut and bruised, being lucky to escape with his life.[3]

In July it was reported that the wages being paid at the mine averaged £3-4 per month, underground men getting around £3 15s. A diagonal shaft, as well as the engine shaft, was 11 fms. below adit. The diagonal would be the drawing shaft, and was being worked by a strongly built horse whim. Sixteen heads of stamps provided pulverised tinstuff for treatment by two round buddles, whose overflow would be arrested by catch-pits on the cliff, so permitting very little tin to escape into the sea. A long, high wall extended from the stamps cliffward with handframes erected under its shelter. Material from the old burrows was being run through the machinery, to test it. The two lodes being worked looked as promising as ever; but the great prospective point was the junction of the three known lodes as they ran from the sea inland. "All mining lore points to large and profitable results just here; and should good fortune attend the spirited proprietors their 'find' will be economically and promptly made marketable at surface."[4]

Unhapilly, this junction was never reached. Some months later the mine ran into financial difficulties. In January 1875, at the suit of merchants, the materials were offered for sale. Apprehending trouble from the miners, who were owed considerable sums in wages, Inspector Pappin, of the County Police, accompanied the auctioneer and the Sheriff of Cornwall's officer to the mine on the day appointed for the sale. They found about seventy men and boys assembled, who offered no resistance to the officials, but refused to allow the auction to begin. In vain did Richards, the auctioneer, plead with them that the law ought to be respected. "They did not strike him, or attempt to—indeed, they mostly kept their hands in their pockets—but they grouped closely together, hustled him, and expressed their determination to prevent a sale at all risks. Seeing that this was a fixed determination the auctioneer and his aides withdrew."

The miners were here following the example recently set by their comrades at Boscaswell Downs, who had reacted in a far stronger manner when faced with a similar situation.[5] It was said that the leniency shown to the Boscaswell men by the authorities after the riot there had encouraged the militants at Morvah Consols; however, they had not the justification of the Boscaswell rioters, since the present sale was being carried out under the authority of the Sheriff, which would ensure an equitable distribution of the proceeds.

It was therefore decided to take action against the ring-leaders. On being threatened with prosecution, the latter sent a letter of apology to the High Sheriff, which was produced in court at Penzance when they were brought before the magistrates. It reads:

"Feb. 22nd, 1875.—We write you this note, to let you know that we, as poor men, and with heavy families, are feeling very much alarmed, finding that we are liable for punishment for the offence we have given to Mr. Hosken Richards, the auctioneer, in the matter of Morvah Consols Mine, that we cannot rest day nor night. Our families are heavy, and must, of course, suffer with their parents. We have not now half meat sufficient for the body; neither can we get work to do that we might get money to supply our families; and if we are taken from them, they must, of course, go to the Workhouse for supply. But we hope that your Honour will be so good towards us, as poor men, to overlook the affair, and pass by the matter, for we are, as aforesaid, sorry from our hearts that we have offended the law, and therefore are liable for punishment; but we one and all, as poor men, do trust that you will pardon us, as far as you are concerned; and therefore, we have signed our hands to this letter, and remain, your obedient servants, one and all, and hope that you will withdraw the summons for us.—Richard Noy, Samuel Veal, William Dymond, John Trembath, Abednego Matthews."

In view of the regret and penitence which they had expressed, the High Sheriff requested the magistrates to withdraw the summons against them which was accordingly done.[5] Those were, indeed, harsh and bitter times for the Cornish miners; one can only marvel that their sufferings did not lead to much greater violence as mine after mine collapsed under the pressure of cheap imported foreign tin.

1. *Cornish Telegraph* July 10 1872
2. *Cornish Telegraph* November 5 1873
3. *Cornish Telegraph* March 25 1874
4. *Cornish Telegraph* July 22 1874
5. *Cornish Telegraph* January 21 and March 10 1875. The story of the Boscaswell riot will be found in Cyril Noall's *The St. Just Mining District,* 1973

WHEAL WHIDDEN

This mine, which formed a part of Morvah and Zennor United, was working independently in March 1849, the purser being W.D. Lawry. A meeting held in Penzance passed accounts showing a credit balance of £80. In September of that year the *Mining Journal* published a picture of a wind machine erected on the mine "some years since."[1]

1. MJ March 3 and September 22 1849. Dines 1956 p. 94